THE ART IS LONG

Also by Frank Forencich:

Exuberant Animal
Beautiful Practice
Change Your Body, Change the World
The Exuberant Animal Collection

THE ART IS LONG

BIG HEALTH AND THE
NEW WARRIOR ACTIVIST

Frank Forencich

Exuberant Animal®

For the Seventh Generation.

CONTENTS

We be of one blood, thee and I.

Rudyard Kipling
The Jungle Book

Origins

Every book needs an origin myth, and every reader wants to know the source of the words before him. What moves this writer? Can we relate to his experience? Can he guide us through this journey of exploration to a destination of insight and meaning? These are essential questions, so let me share the path that brought me here.

I've had some powerful adventures in my 60-plus years, but my story is not unusual. As children, all of us thrive in the outdoors. We love the world of sunlight, dirt, plants, animals, sky, and water. We delight in our sports and our bodies grow strong. The world makes perfect physical sense to us. But later, things change and we're forced to come to grips with the perplexing and often body-hostile demands of the modern world. Suddenly, the world no longer seems so friendly and we struggle to find a way.

My journey began in a mountain valley near Lake Tahoe in the Sierra Nevada Mountains of California. I was perhaps seven years old at the time. It was a glorious summer day and our family was camped beside a beautiful alpine river. As I explored the riverbank, I discovered a wonderland of boulders—gorgeous granite blocks that were both smooth and rough, clean and inviting. I climbed and scrambled, and suddenly, I was struck with the most powerful realization of my young life, a personal Zen moment that has stayed with me for over five decades.

At first contact with the granite, I was overcome with pleasure as my hands, feet and knees touched the gorgeous orbs. I was delighted and astonished that something could feel so right for my body. My muscles rejoiced; the shapes were perfect for pushing, pulling, climbing, and jumping. It was like the playground at my elementary school, only a thousand times better. I was struck by the improbable coincidence that these boulders, this river—this world—seemed to be made just for me, for my body. Every detail of the outer world seemed an ideal match with every detail of my anatomy. My joy was boundless; I belonged to this place.

Not surprisingly, the boulders continued to draw me back, even after my family and I returned home to what would later be called Silicon Valley. As my body matured, I returned to the Sierras at every opportunity; hiking, scrambling, and climbing the walls in Yosemite. I loved the granitic world and it loved me back. My body became strong and my spirit soared.

But sadly, the joy of my first alpine contact was later eclipsed by an equal and opposite experience, a toxic event that has repeated itself thousands of times in my adult life. This time I was stuck in traffic somewhere south of Oakland, boxed in by a pod of monstrous 18-wheelers, incarcerated in a cage of metal, glass, and plastic. The summertime heat was intense, and the exhaust savaged my lungs and eyes. All I could see were cars, trucks, concrete retaining walls and outdoor advertising—no plants, no animals, no color, no texture. Not only was my world lifeless, noisy, and hostile, but I was utterly powerless to change it or escape. Stress hormones flooded my bloodstream and my spirit raged.

As I fought back against my predicament, a voice rose up through my frantic consciousness: "My body is not made for this! This place is not made for my body!" My tissue screamed, "This is profoundly, fundamentally wrong! It is wrong by a million years! I hate it, and I am right to hate it!" I felt, quite literally, like a misfit in the world. And to make matters worse, I felt alone in my suffering. It wasn't until years later that I began to realize that a great many people share my angst. In fact, millions of us are misfits, built for the wild and out of place with the world that we've created. There's a reason we feel the way we do.

Thus began my study of the human body and our mismatched predicament. In the years that followed, I became a dedicated student of the human animal. I studied martial art for many years and relished the disciplined play of karate and aikido. As an undergraduate at Stanford, I learned about human evolution and our deep continuities with habitat and culture. I even visited Africa a few times to learn about human ancestry and the ways of native people. Later, I attended massage school and studied with a series of masterful trainers, coaches, and physical therapists. The body, I began to discover, was vast and endlessly engaging.

In the early days, my aspirations were pretty conventional. I wanted to excel in sports, climb big mountains, and move my body with speed, power, and athleticism. I sought fitness, mastery, and achievement. But over the years, my path began to turn in some surprising ways. As I looked deeper into the human experience, I came to realize that health is far bigger than I had supposed. Far more than a matter of diet and exercise, it's about continuity with larger life processes of tribe, nature, and culture. In this sense, the "I" was far less important than I had thought. In fact, the "me" turned out to be kind of a sideshow.

This was a powerful insight, but it was also highly disruptive. Suddenly, my personal ambitions for sporting achievement no longer seemed so compelling. My quest for personal mastery began to feel isolating and even self-defeating. The more I focused on my personal welfare, the more I became separate from the source of life. To be truly healthy, I needed to integrate more completely with the world around me.

But of course, this also put me on a divergent course with modern culture. The more I learned about the interdependent nature of my body and the relentless destruction of the natural world, the more distressed I became. To me, the facts were becoming obvious: The health of the human body is ultimately dependent on the health of habitat and community. And yet, this connection is almost universally ignored in modern health disciplines where biomedical reductionism rules the day. Human health and environmental preservation are treated as entirely

4

different fields, with miles of empty space between them. We treat the body like an isolated medical object, a mechanism to be studied, tweaked, and repaired. At the same time, we treat the natural world like an economic resource to be exploited at will.

This disconnect nagged at me day and night, begging for an explanation and a resolution. And the more I learned, the more anxious and angry I became. Why are we ignoring the basic fact of interdependence? Why are we so relentless in our destruction of the very thing that gives us life? Why are we so passive in the face of biospheric catastrophe? Where is the outrage?

My anxiety reached a fever pitch with the American presidential election of 2016. Far more distressing than politics as usual, I felt this outcome as a historic rejection of interdependence and intelligence, a spasm of self-defeating behavior. Just at the time when we're in such desperate need of ecological and social wisdom, we saw fit to elect a man and a party with no appreciation for history, nature, or the planet as a whole. I experienced this event as a genuine trauma, one that reverberated in every cell of my body. A sense of grief coursed through my veins and settled into my organs.

And it wasn't just me; millions of people around the world experienced similar angst. The election of Donald Trump was more than just an affront to dignity and democratic processes. The cabinet appointments and executive orders of January 2017 battered our spirits and our sense of hope for the future. The assault on the Environmental Protection Agency was an attack on our core values and our future. The defeat at Standing Rock came as a crushing body blow. The approval of the Keystone

5

XL pipeline and the rejection of landmark progress on climate change added yet another layer of injury. It's too soon to say for certain, but it's likely that the Trump victory has had widespread negative effects on human health, not just in our country, but around the planet. When our spirits are in anguish, our bodies cannot be far behind.

Today, I write as a tribal elder. I write from a place of frustration, anger, and distress, but also from a place of ferocious curiosity and commitment. I am fascinated with human adaptation and resilience in the face of challenge. I am intrigued with the challenge of mismatch, the disconnect between ancient bodies and the modern world. And most of all, I am curious about the intersection of health and activism: where it comes from, how to promote it, and how to preserve it in times of crisis. If we can understand the relationships that unify health, the body, and the natural world, we can move in a new direction. I offer this book as an antidote to our mismatch, our trauma, and our crisis of leadership. This book is for all us misfits. No one book can change everything, but this may be a start.

The State of the Animal

In effect, humans have dragged a body with a long hominid history into an overfed, malnourished, sedentary, sunlight-deficient, sleep-deprived, competitive, inequitable, and socially-isolating environment with dire consequences.

Sebastian Junger
Tribe: On Homecoming and Belonging

We are continually faced with a series of great opportunities brilliantly disguised as insoluble problems.

John Gardener

In the beginning, life takes us by surprise. If we're lucky, that surprise is a pleasant one. We attach securely to a caregiver, our elders protect us from danger, and our tribe provides us with the essentials we need to grow. Our neighborhood is a safe home base to explore, and our childhood becomes a wonderland of play, discovery, and learning. Health comes naturally, sleep is deep, and our pleasures are profound. The world is friendly.

But after a few short years, we're thrust out the door into another reality with a far different look and feel. Suddenly, the modern world overwhelms us with complexity and an unpredictable, sometimes brutal mix of opportunity and danger. This world pulls us in a thousand directions, and we scramble to keep up. The world, it seems, may not be so friendly after all.

Our distress is reflected in our bodies. Today we're suffering from all manner of lifestyle diseases, including obesity, diabetes, heart disease, and neurological disorders. We're surrounded by magical laborsaving technologies and powerful systems that should be making our lives easier and more enjoyable, but at the same time, many of us are feeling stressed, fearful, anxious, and depressed. We wonder why our bodies and our spirits are in pain. We wonder why our lives hurt so much.

For many, just making it through a typical day is an onerous challenge. There's never enough time to do what needs to be done, and a crushing sense of urgency drives us to distraction. We spend our days running from one emergency to the next, with scarcely enough time to take care of ourselves or savor the mystery of our existence. In the chaos, many of us have fallen out of touch with the primal forces and processes that nourish us and keep us whole.

We feel it in our guts, in our minds, and in our spirits: Something is terribly, tragically wrong. At scales both large and small, the modern world feels exceedingly fragile. We see it in our movies and in the faces of people we meet. Anxiety courses through our conversations, our bloodstreams, even our dreams. We worry about our health, our jobs, and our families. We're troubled about terrorism, economic collapse and the fate of the biosphere. Doubts about the future keep us up at night and haunt us during the day.

We are right to feel this way. We live in an age of spectacular progress, educational affluence, and technological power. We're awash in knowledge of every description, equipped with the most advanced tools ever created, surrounded by outrageous opportunity and potential at every turn. At the same time, many of us are mired in confusion, ill health, anxiety, depression, and isolation. We've created a world of incredible power and convenience, and yet we seem exceedingly uncomfortable with actually living in it. As the comedian Louis C.K. put it, "Everything's amazing, but nobody's happy."

the earth hurts

Our predicament presses in from every direction. Our primal relationships with habitat, tribe, and body have been stretched almost to the breaking point. No longer do we live on or even near the land that supports us; we are divorced from the Earth, living in isolation from the natural processes that sustain us. Even as we try to keep our minds focused on our work, our families, and the brighter side of modern living, the threat of planetary-scale events creeps into our bodies and minds. Even the uninformed are haunted by a creeping feeling that we've already gone too far, that we're already living in an era of ecological

9

overshoot. Every living system in the biosphere is suffering. We live, as Aldo Leopold famously put it in *A Sand County Almanac,* "in a world of wounds."

The pain is around us and in us. Human impact on the Earth is so significant that we are now classified as a geologic force. Today we live in the Anthropocene, an entirely new epoch dominated by human manipulation of habitat. Human beings have now co-opted more than 50 percent of the planet's surface for their own uses. According to the United Nations Environment Programme, our global footprint is about one and half times the Earth's capacity to provide our basic needs: "If nothing changes, with an increasing population that could reach 9.6 billion by 2050, we will need almost three planets to sustain our ways of living."

The brutal environmental facts are well known, even as they are often denied. Climate change is a factual reality. In January 2017, the National Oceanic and Atmospheric Administration released its annual State of the Climate report, finding that 2016 was the hottest year on record since scientists started tracking global temperatures in 1880. Of the seventeen hottest years on record, sixteen have occurred since 2000. And a recent study reveals that tens of thousands of miles of permafrost in northwest Canada are rapidly melting, adding weight to recent research showing an accelerating decline in permafrost in Alaska, Siberia, and Scandinavia.

As this book goes to print, an immense carbon bomb is going off in Alberta, Canada. This Tar Sands "Gigaproject" is one of the largest industrial projects in human history— and one of the most destructive. Tar sands mining releases at least three times the carbon dioxide emissions as regular oil production, and is probably the single largest industrial contributor in North America to climate change. This is the second fastest rate of deforestation on the planet after the Amazon Rainforest Basin. The operation consumes immense amounts of fresh water and leaves behind gigantic lakes of toxic sludge.

Global sea ice is now at a record low. In December 2016, scientists released the so-called "Arctic Report Card," which noted that "The Arctic is warming at least twice as fast as the rest of the planet." This forms a perilous feedback loop: As ice melts, darker water and land absorb more of the sun's heat, which of course means more melting, and so on...

Even the most conservative climate projections mean massive disruptions, if not outright catastrophe for millions of people around the world. Entire cities will probably have to be abandoned. Mass migration will become commonplace. In 2016, James Hansen, a leading voice in climate science, shared his assessment in the journal *Atmospheric Chemistry and Physics*:

> If the ocean continues to accumulate heat and increase melting of marine-terminating ice shelves of Antarctica and Greenland, a point will be reached at which it is impossible to avoid large-scale ice sheet disintegration with sea level rise of at least several meters. The economic and social cost of losing functionality of all coastal cities is practically incalculable.

Our planet, you might say, is on thin ice.

Even worse, we are now in the midst of an epic, planet-wide extinction crisis, one that rivals the most massive extinction events in the history of life. In her 2014 book *The Sixth Extinction: An Unnatural History*, Elizabeth Kolbert estimates flora and fauna loss by the end of the 21st century to be between 20 and 50 percent of all living species on Earth. Biologist E. O. Wilson suggests that the extinction rate is now about "1,000 times faster than before the global spread of humanity."

Tragically, this trend includes our closest primate relatives. Populations of chimps, bonobos, gorillas, and orangutans are all under severe pressure. A report released in January 2017 found that 60 percent of primate species are now threatened with extinction and 75 percent have declining populations. If current trends continue, these species will likely go extinct, leaving us as the sole surviving ape on the planet.

We see the same worrisome trends across the entire biosphere: fresh water depletion, eroding topsoil, over-fishing, deforestation, and fragmentation of entire ecosystems. Wherever we look, habitat is in trouble. A typical flight in a light aircraft reveals the carnage. With development almost everywhere, there's almost no place left for animals to make a living. In a very real sense, an enormous percentage of life on Earth must now be categorized as homeless.

Even the Vatican recognizes the urgency of the threat. A February 2017 report, "How to Save the Natural World on Which We Depend," takes a no-nonsense approach to over-development, climate change, overpopulation, and unsustainable agricultural practices. "The living fabric of the world [...] is slipping through our fingers without our showing much sign of caring," warn the authors.

Taken together, the combined weight of climate change, ecosystem degradation, and the continued threat of nuclear weapons cast a deep shadow over the human experience. In January 2017, the Bulletin of the Atomic Scientists marked the seventieth anniversary of its Doomsday Clock on Thursday by moving it thirty seconds closer to midnight. This is the closest to midnight that the clock has been since 1953.

our bodies hurt

The state of the planet reverberates through every cell of our bodies. Even when we succeed at putting large-scale global events out of mind, our bodies still feel the pain of the world. It's no exaggeration to say that we are traumatized. As the noted ecopsychologist Theodore Roszak put it, "The Earth hurts and we hurt with it."

If this diagnosis sounds like mere poetry, think again. In fact, the effect is similar to the reaction that takes place in the bodies of sports fans, whose hormone levels rise and fall with the fate of their favorite teams. If your team loses the big game, your testosterone levels drop. Likewise, heart attacks are more common in the days after a major playoff loss. The pain of losing is real. Your team hurts, and you hurt with it.

The same pattern plays out in our relationships with families and friends. When a loved one is suffering, we experience pain as well. Hormone levels wax and wane as we feel what the people around us are feeling. When our families and communities hurt, we hurt with them.

If you happen to be even a casual "fan" of nature and the earth, you're going to experience the same kind of physical effects, but at a far deeper level than with a sporting contest. After all, our relationship with the planet is primordial. We've been evolving and living in tandem with this "team" for the last several million years, a relationship of deepest possible intimacy. Every detail of our anatomy and physiology grew out of this relationship. And our "home team" is taking a beating.

Given the state of our world, it comes as no surprise to learn that humanity is also experiencing a rapid and ominous increase in so-called non-communicable diseases. Also referred to as "lifestyle diseases" or "diseases of civilization," these conditions include obesity, diabetes, heart disease, cancer, depression, and respiratory disease. The World Health Organization reports that non-communicable diseases (NCDs) are the leading cause of mortality in the world, representing over 60 percent of all deaths. Currently, NCDs kills thirty-six million people a year, a number that is expected to rise by 17 to 24 percent within the next decade. The NCD Alliance, an advocacy and outreach organization, describes lifestyle disease as "a global emergency."

The statistics are ominous. We now know that some 60 percent of the American population is either overweight or obese, a trend that is reflected in growing numbers worldwide. Some seventy-nine million Americans over the age of twenty have prediabetes; up to 70 percent of them will go on to develop diabetes.

Experts predict that by 2050, the number of adults with diabetes will reach one in three.

But lifestyle disease is no ordinary epidemic. The physical condition of modern humanity is a radical departure from our normal state of health. Throughout our hunter-gatherer past, and a big chunk of modern history as well, physical vitality has been the norm. Infectious disease extracted a frightening toll on millions of people, but for those who could avoid infection, physicality was robust. Native people, farmers, explorers, and settlers tended to be strong and resilient, far more robust than the average person of the modern world. Not so long ago, we were outrageously healthy, wild animals, but today, disease has become a new, and very disturbing "normal."

our lives hurt

There's a lot more to our predicament than the health and disease of our physical bodies. There's something extremely painful about the totality of our lives. Almost everything feels fragile and uncertain. The world's systems—biological, social, economic, and governmental—feel like an immense house of cards on the verge of collapse.

For many, stress has become a 24/7 experience. Our primal bodies know something is wrong, but we can't say precisely what it is. We are increasingly on edge, primed for action, simulta-neously excited, vigilant, fearful, exhausted, anxious, and de-pressed. The challenges just keep coming, and even worse, stress and fear are piped into our homes, our cars, and our brains in every waking moment. We know the details of collapsing nations, economies, and ecosystems thousands of miles away. This is stress on a scale never seen before in human history.

Most of us are suffering the combined effects of onerous workplace demands, interruptive technology and high-speed communication. This adds up to a planet-wide disruption of human attention. Almost everything we do is now classified as urgent. Technology has taken on a life of its own, constantly generating new forms that make previous forms obsolete. Speed has become a goal in and of itself, independent of any other objective. We go faster simply because we can.

The new digital world is proving to be a potent source of anxiety. Every day brings a new story of corporate data breach, and even our elections appear vulnerable to hacking. The threat of identity theft looms large, with personal or business catastrophe just a click away. And lurking in the background is the specter of mass unemployment. Futurists now believe that artificial intelligence will soon automate vast sectors of our economy. Millions of people may well lose their jobs.

Adding to our burden is the yawning chasm between rich and poor. Nearly everyone has heard about the income gap, but the consequences extend far beyond mere disparities in wealth. For all practical purposes, the rich and the poor now live in radically different habitats. Communities are "gated," by physical, financial, digital, and cultural barriers. Increasingly, rich and poor people simply don't come in contact with one another. Social inequality is a threat to everyone in the modern world, the wealthy included.

Levels of social distrust, meanwhile, are high at an all-time high. A generation ago, about half of all Americans felt the people around them could be trusted, but today less than a third do so. According to a Pew Research study of social trends, only about 19 percent of millennials believe other people can be trusted. Likewise, trust in government and financial systems is eroding, and capitalism is looking more and more like a reverse Robin Hood system. As the gulf between rich and poor widens, it's becoming obvious that our current system only serves the needs of a select few. In the face of this escalating uncertainty, a new generation of "preppers" has essentially given up on society and retreated to remote regions to build their own self-sufficient homes.

Political polarization and extremism are increasing around the world. Across the spectrum, people are furious. "Anger rooms" are popping up in urban centers, where customers can vent their frustrations with bats and clubs by beating inanimate objects and manikins into pieces. At the same time, we're suffering a marked increase in loneliness, isolation, and alienation, and our fear is reflected in a new security culture. Cameras are everywhere, and computers are busy tracking our every keystroke. Facial recognition software lurks in public spaces, watchers always at work.

An appalling number of people are now homeless and even stateless. According to the United Nations High Commissioner for Refugees, "We are now witnessing the highest levels of displacement on record." To put it in stark, global terms: "One in every 122 humans is now either a refugee, internally displaced, or seeking asylum." Sixty-five million people have been forcibly displaced people worldwide. The mass influx of migrants into Europe in recent years has put incredible pressure on social, economic, and governmental systems. According to the International Organization for Migration, over 1 million people arrived in Europe in 2015. Thousands of people die each year attempting to cross the Mediterranean.

Suffering under the combined weight of ecological breakdown and chaotic social change, many of us have begun to feel powerless and, even worse, irrelevant. As individuals, we are dwarfed by giant corporations, government institutions, and forces of culture that seem to do as they please. We attempt to speak up, but our complaints are simply processed by automated systems, then filed away in databases to be forgotten. This sense of powerlessness eventually leads to a state of learned helplessness and psychic numbing.

Our dislocation and isolation from the natural world weighs our bodies and spirits. Some observers describe our disordered relationship with habitat as *solastalgia,* a term coined by Australian philosopher Glenn Albrecht. The word refers to psychic or existential distress caused by environmental change. Albrecht studied the experiences of persistent drought and large-scale open-cut coal mining on individuals in Australia. In both cases, people exposed to environmental change experienced negative emotions, exacerbated by a sense of powerlessness and a lack of control.

Albrecht calls solastalgia "a new type of sadness," but it's clearly reminiscent of the trauma experienced by native people around the world. In both cases, it feels like the earth is being pulled out from under us. Our familiar markers of habitat, the physical and sensory signals that define our home, are vanishing. Our world is moving away from us and we miss it terribly. For those of us who are witness to environmental devastation, solastalgia is "The homesickness you feel when you're still at home." According to Albrecht, "You feel dislocated, but you haven't gone anywhere."

Albrecht and other ecopsychologists warn of a worldwide increase in ecosystem distress syndromes. We are reaching a "tipping point in our heads" he says. And of course, since mind, body, and spirit are intimately connected, it's fair to say that we're reaching a tipping point in our health and hearts as well.

It remains to be seen whether the diagnosis of solastalgia will be embraced by the medical community or given the clinical significance it deserves. Skeptics may well demand hard evidence of a body-habitat connection, but even a modest familiarity with human history makes the case. We are of the Earth. Of course the destruction of the natural world would be reflected in the state of our bodies and our minds. It would be bizarre if it were any other way.

In any case, we are now suffering immense psycho-spiritual stress. Globally, more than 350 million people of all ages suffer from depression. The World Health Organization predicts that depression will soon be the second leading cause of disability, after heart disease. Depression has now surpassed HIV/AIDS, malaria, diabetes, and war as the leading cause of disability worldwide. Over eight hundred thousand people die by suicide every year.

Anxiety and depression now afflict both young and old. According to a report by NPR in September 2016, as many as one in five school-age children suffer from some form of mental illness. According to a 2013 survey by the American College Health Association, "57 percent of female and 40 percent of male college students reported feeling overwhelmingly anxious, while 33 percent of females and 27 percent of males reported feeling seriously depressed." The association also found that suicide rates in young adults had tripled since the 1950s, with the National Alliance on Mental Illness estimating that a quarter of college students have had suicidal thoughts.

Not only are we anxious and depressed, but we're also suffering a planet-wide epidemic of disordered sleep and insomnia. Studies show that Americans get less sleep than they need, and that this sleep is of dubious quality. Health journalists remind us that poor sleep quality makes us vulnerable to a host of personal health problems, but the consequences extend deep into society and culture. When we're sleep-deprived, we're far more likely to fall back on habitual thoughts, inclinations, and behaviors. We're less likely to expose ourselves to novelty or ask challenging questions about ourselves or the world. And when entire populations are sleep-deprived, our collective ability to see the world clearly becomes massively compromised. In this respect, sleep deprivation isn't just a threat to individual health; it's a threat to entire human systems.

To compound things, a staggering number of us are also in chronic psychophysical pain. The abuse of painkillers now claims the lives of more Americans than heroin and cocaine combined, and the number of Americans who die from prescription drug overdoses has more than tripled since the late 1990s. Public health officials have called the current opioid epidemic the worst drug crisis in American history. Since 2000, more than three hundred thousand Americans have lost their lives to an opioid overdose. In September 2016, NPR reported a study that almost half of all Americans take prescription painkillers, tranquilizers, stimulants, or sedatives.

A 2016 report from the Surgeon General highlights the pain that people are experiencing. Among the findings: "More people use prescription opioids than use tobacco. There are more people with substance abuse disorders than people with cancer." The study also reported that in 2015, sixty-six million people reported that they'd engaged in at least one episode of binge drinking in the previous month…Alcohol misuse contributes to eighty-eight thousand deaths in the United States each year; one in ten deaths among working adults are due to alcohol misuse. Obviously, this is no mere substance abuse problem. It reflects a widespread inability to adapt to the conditions of the modern world. Adam Alter, author of *Irresistible: Why We Can't Stop Checking, Scrolling, Clicking and Watching*, estimates that roughly half the population of the developed world is addicted to something: substances, devices, or experiences.

All of this angst adds up to a profound crisis of meaning for modern humans. In this ambiguous and often painful world, many of us are failing to find a sense of relevance or purpose. With a planet in peril, is my life or profession making a difference? Are my efforts helping anyone or anything? Am I having an impact, or am I making things worse? In many professions, this is a truly open question. When everything is in flux, it's hard to know the power or appropriateness of our actions.

Our predicament would sound familiar to Viktor Frankl, author of *Man's Search for Meaning*. For Frankl, the quest to find a sense of meaning is the essence of human motivation, a basic striving that he calls the "will to meaning." He also believed that the conditions of modern society leave many individuals with a feeling of meaninglessness—an affliction he called an *existential vacuum*. When this condition remains unresolved, individuals are said to "lack the awareness of a meaning worth living for. They are haunted by the experience of their inner emptiness, a void within themselves."

In a very real sense, we no longer know who we are as a species. As theologian Thomas Berry put it, we are "between stories." Anthropologists tell us that we are hunter-gatherers at our core, struggling to adapt our legacy programming to the demands of a modern, alien environment. At the same time, futurists tell us that our destiny lies with technology and the colonization of space. Some of us desperately want to go back while others claim that our problems are only minor glitches on the road to a prosperous future. In *The Social Conquest of Earth,* Edward O. Wilson put it this way:

> We have created a Star Wars civilization, with Stone Age emotions, medieval institutions, and godlike technology.

We thrash about. We are terribly confused by the mere fact of our existence, and a danger to ourselves and to the rest of life.

We struggle to know ourselves. We'd like to look on the bright side, but our conversations are laced with grim metaphors and dark humor. Some people describe modern human activity as "a war on nature." Some say that we're living on a time bomb. Biologist Lynn Margulis has called us "bipedal weeds." Others describe us as "a cancer on the earth." Some have claimed that "we are the asteroid." Obviously, we're beginning to have some grave misgivings about who we are and what we're doing in the world.

mismatch and misfits

For casual observers, the suffering of the modern human body and spirit seems arbitrary or just plain incomprehensible. Frustrated and frightened, we attempt to pin the blame on whatever's handy—individual events, actors, processes, or organizations. We're victims of poisonous substances, opposing tribes, bad policies, corporate greed, or the agriculture–industrial complex. Something "out there" is making us sick.

But when we take a longer view, we begin to see something more fundamental at work. The human animal now lives in a strange and unfamiliar world. Our bodies, sculpted by millions of years of evolution, are not just ancient. They are prehistorical. Our anatomy, physiology, and psychology are adapted to life in a wild, outdoor environment. At our core, we are hunters and gatherers, primed for life in natural habitat. But today we're attempting to live in world that many anthropologists call an "alien environment."

This disconnect is often described as "the mismatch hypothesis" or simply "mismatch." In academic circles, biologists call it "the evolutionary discordance hypothesis." But whatever you call it, this gap between our evolutionary heritage and modern life is a truly wicked, unprecedented problem, one that begs for an explanation and a resolution.

The problem comes into stark relief when we compare our ancestral living conditions with what we're experiencing in this modern, alien world. It wasn't that long ago that we lived most of our lives outdoors. Conditions were often harsh, but our bodies were good at adapting. In contrast, we now live in an artificially constructed world that's isolated from the very processes and systems that sustain our health. Many modern people go weeks, months, or years without any meaningful contact with plants, animals, soil, or natural light. The continuities that normally sustain us have been largely severed.

Our alien environment challenges our health in myriad ways. Most obviously, it encourages sedentary "living." Powerful machines and vehicles deprive us of essential physical challenge, leading to atrophy and diseases of under-use. Sedentary living even weakens our brains and our spirits. Inactivity diminishes the production of vital neurotrophic hormones that are essential for optimal neurological function.

Thanks to work by neuroscientist Kelly Lambert at Randolph–Macon College, we now know that the human brain is organized around an "efforts-based reward system." That is, there are powerful linkages between the movement and pleasure centers in the brain. In normal, ancestral conditions, we move our bodies and then receive a reward, usually food. But when the reward comes without effort, the circuit is violated. Over time, this can lead to depression, lethargy, and apathy. This is why struggle and striving are so important for human functioning and happiness.

Unfortunately, the modern world often gives us rewards without effort. In a physical sense, life has become far too easy. Most obviously, our food has become almost entirely disconnected from muscular effort. For the vast majority of human history, we worked hard, then relished the fruits of our hunting and gathering labors. Ancient brain circuitry responded with a burst of neurotransmitters and in turn, a sense of pleasure.

But today our agricultural–industrial system has given us food so cheap and readily available that, from the body's point of view, it's essentially free. If you've got a working credit card, all you have to do is swipe and eat.

Like astronauts, we now eat an abstracted diet that can only be described as "space food." In the vast majority of cases, we have no idea where our food comes from. It just appears in our supermarkets or on our restaurant tables with no connection to the land or the people who prepared it. The ancient connections between physical movement, people and food have been severed by high-efficiency systems, fossil fueled transport and computerized management. Our food no longer bonds us to the land or one another.

Our alien environment also subjects us to profound sensory distortion. On one hand, we're assaulted by a flood of hyper-normal stimuli, sensations intentionally engineered to go beyond the normal range of human experience. At the same time, our sense of touch is under-stimulated. The demise of physical labor and craft, along with the disappearance of handwriting, has led to an atrophy of this crucial sensory feedback system.

At the same time, we're suffering under a tidal wave of acoustic pollution. We treat the acoustic commons the same way that we treat our atmosphere and our oceans: as a dumping ground for the byproducts of human activity. Some of us manage to adapt to the din, but the consequences to body, mind, and spirit are immense.

Chronic noise is now considered an authentic and pervasive threat to human health. Noise has been linked to hearing impairment, hypertension, heart disease, sleep disturbance, and anxiety. Noise exposure has also been linked to immune system dysfunctions and birth defects. A World Health Organization report on the "Burden of Disease from Environmental Noise" concluded that "Western Europeans suffer a heavy toll of death and disability through exposure to excessive noise, making it second only to air pollution as an environmental cause of ill health." Elevated noise levels can create stress, increase workplace accident rates, and stimulate aggression and other anti-social behaviors.

Our health is further challenged by the hyper-clean nature of today's environments. We scrub every surface with antimicrobial agents, depriving our immune systems of the stimulation they need to develop and remain strong. The "hygiene hypothesis" tells us that the human body needs contact with soil, plants, and animals, but we persist in sanitizing every available surface.

Light now assaults us almost continuously. Darkness, once a primal feature of human experience, is fast disappearing. Artificial light obscures starlight, and disrupts ecosystems and human physiology. The Milky Way, the most awe-inspiring sight in human history, is no longer visible to most people around the world.

Taken together, our alien environment gives our bodies highly conflicting signals of challenge, threat, safety, and nurturing. Stimuli are often random, and our bodies are jerked in many directions simultaneously. In this sense, life in our modern world resembles a really bad movie. Imagine a film called *Mixed Message*: The action opens as a urban romantic comedy, then abruptly shifts to a violent action flick set in outer space. Then it turns into a documentary about school reform in nineteenth-century England, then jumps to some soft-core porno. Just when that starts to get interesting, it shifts to a preview for an animated Pixar cartoon, then concludes with a heartwarming sequence about a boy and his dog.

Naturally, you walk out of the theatre confused and disgusted. There was no coherence to the experience, no consistent storyline you could relate to. But if your mind and spirit felt disintegrated, think about what that disconnected narrative meant for your body. One minute you're pumping oxytocin in response to the warm and fuzzy romantic comedy, the next minute you're mainlining adrenaline. Romance, then fear, then sexual excitement, then intellectual analysis. With no narrative thread to hold it all together, your body never knew where it was going.

Thankfully, the movie is over in an hour or two, but in today's world we experience a much more prolonged version of sensory chaos. This leads to *autonomic confusion,* the widespread disintegration of the human mind–body system, driven by disconnected stimuli, ideas, and images. One moment our bodies are preparing for anticipated conflict, the next they're trying to enter the anabolic phase of tissue rebuilding. Our tissue and organs are continuously jerked around by a narrative that can't make up its mind. Naturally, this is hard on our health and our sanity. The random, mixed messages of the modern world scramble our physiology and our peace of mind.

In essence, the problem of the modern world is one of disintegration. The ancient human body is a collection of sub-systems, each with its own evolutionary history. We are a collection of component parts, sometimes called a "kludge." In normal, ancestral circumstances, most of these component parts work together in synchrony and we remain healthy. But if the kludge is left unchallenged by inactivity or driven in different directions by the chaotic stimuli of an alien environment, these components can drift apart in function. Weakness and disease is the result.

As you can see, mismatch is no trivial curiosity. While many of us have heard about mismatch theory and the "cavemen with cell phones" meme, it's easy to underestimate the magnitude and consequences of the challenge. Most people simply haven't given much thought to human ancestry or how different the modern world is from ancestral conditions. Our neuroplastic brains are really good at adjusting to conditions, so many of us simply suppose that the world we live in today is "normal." But from an evolutionary standpoint, the modern world is something else altogether.

Our failure to recognize the challenge of mismatch causes us an extreme level of grief and confusion. Many of us are inclined to suppose that we ought to know what we're doing in this world. And when we struggle to adapt, we conclude that it's our own personal failing. We blame ourselves. We conclude that we just aren't smart enough, strong enough, disciplined enough, or beautiful enough.

But the art of navigating mismatch is a very long one indeed. The idea that any of us should know how to live in the modern world is preposterous. Our predicament is historically unprecedented. Today we live in a world in which some of our deepest, most powerful instincts are incompatible with success. Some of our ancestral programming is valuable and will guide us in the right direction, but other impulses can lead us wildly astray. And it's not altogether clear which are which.

Today's world may well look "normal" to the untrained eye, but to an evolutionary biologist, it is alien in almost every dimension. From a historical standpoint, being born into mismatch is like being thrown into deep, cold water. Your body has some of the capabilities it needs to function, but it's far from a perfect match. You can swim for a while, maybe even enjoy the experience for a time, but sooner or later something will have to give. It's no wonder that so many of us are struggling. Mismatch can be a real bitch.

meet the canary

For many observers of the human condition, it's tempting to dismiss the diseased state of the human body as a simple, fixable medical issue. Yes, millions of people are suffering from obesity, diabetes, depression, chronic pain and a host of stress-related disorders, but these are biomedical afflictions of the body, nothing more. They are regrettable, but do not affect the bigger pictures of our lives. If we apply enough medical resources to the problem, we can make it go away.

But this view is shortsighted. In fact, the implications of lifestyle disease go far beyond the dysfunction of tissues and organs. These diseases are not just of the body, but also of the mind, spirit, and society. The body, in other words, is talking to us, telling us that something is tragically wrong with the way we're living. In fact, our bodies are canaries in the coal mine of the modern world. They are screaming out, calling us to change. In this sense, we are our own "sentinel species."

In the conventional, biological sense, sentinel species are animals used to provide advance warning of danger. Canaries are the classic example. The idea traces back to 1913, when Scottish physiologist John Scott Haldane proposed placing a canary in a mine to detect carbon monoxide. Similarly, conservation biologists speak of "indicator species"—plants, birds, and animals that are so typical of a habitat or ecosystem that their condition is an indicator of the condition of the whole.

The value of sentinel or indicator species lies in the warning they provide. But in our situation, we are mostly failing to heed the message. Instead, we opt to treat the canary with all manner of "solutions." We build vast medical industries to improve the welfare of the canary. We put the canary on special diets. We perform bariatric surgery on the canary. We give it counseling and behavior modification programs. We spend billions to develop new medications and gene therapies to treat the canary's condition. And of course, some of us profit immensely from treating the canary's condition. Perversely, a diseased canary is good for the economy.

Meanwhile, the fitness industry is hard at work trying to build a better canary. Trainers help the canary lose weight, build muscle, and improve its athletic performance. Experts and coaches help canaries appear attractive to one another. We display images of slender, muscular canaries on the covers of our magazines. And if the canary looks good, everyone is happy.

All the while, we ignore context. We spare no expense in keeping the canary alive and "healthy," but we reject the suggestion that we might do something about conditions inside the mine. Taken by itself, the canary's epidemic of depression alone should grab our attention and force an intensive re-examination of our predicament. If an alien power had come to earth and inflicted a similar carnage on our bodies and spirit, we would presumably fight back.

When dealing with living organisms, context matters enormously, a fact vividly illustrated in Bruce Alexander's legendary "rat park" studies. As a young researcher in the 1970s, Alexander was struck by the fact that most studies of addiction were carried out on isolated rodents in cages. Cocaine and other "addictive substances" were introduced to the rodents and many became addicted. But Alexander objected that the rats were living in an unnatural environment and therefore, the results could not be trusted. To test his theory, he built an enriched environment in his laboratory, complete with everything a rodent might desire: natural features, room to move and companions to play with. When he later introduced the so-called "addictive substances," few of the animals became addicted.

Naturally, some scientists dispute Alexander's work, but his results are highly suggestive and consistent with our own experience. Of course context matters. Of course our bodies behave differently in alien environments. Of course there are health and behavior consequences when we're forced to live outside our evolutionary range. Just ask any dog owner. Force your pet to live in isolation for a few weeks and you'll see some serious behavior problems. There's nothing wrong with your dog. The problem is with his world.

Likewise, our problem lies not with the canary, but with the world we're creating. The reason the canary is suffering is because its world is out of alignment with its evolutionary nature; the canary is mismatched to its environment. If we fail to address the larger context of the canary's life, all our medical and fitness interventions will be for naught. And thus the core message of this book: Heed the canary.

new problems, old solutions

Unfortunately, our conventional public health remedies are failing to make much of a difference. Most of our institutional programs are aimed at the historical challenges of infectious disease, and for good reason. Infectious disease is easily the single most destructive adversary that we've had to face as a species. Plagues of the Black Death, smallpox, tuberculosis, and the flu have killed millions upon millions of people, far more than have died from any other cause. We were right to create institutions, programs, and philosophies dedicated to fighting this fight.

But as the old saw goes, the military is always fighting the last war, and so too in the world of modern health and medicine. Infectious disease remains a threat and probably always will be, but lifestyle disease calls for an entirely new set of ideas and orientations. What works against an infectious microbe is unlikely to work against a mismatched relationship with the modern world. You can treat a bacteria or a virus like an adversary, but what are we to do when the adversary is our own behavior—or worse still, our own culture?

To add to the difficulty, we're medicalizing a vast swath of the human experience. It wasn't long ago that medicine was almost totally ineffective, for any condition. Prior to the age of antiseptics and antibiotics, almost nothing worked, strictly speaking, for any disease. But beginning in the 1940s, penicillin became widely available, and medicine was forever changed. No longer a supplemental practice that might occasionally ease a patient's suffering, medicine began a steep ascendance in power and respectability. Suddenly, medicine offered the prospect of curing all diseases and afflictions. Never again would we have to suffer pain, illness, or discomfort.

As our expectations of medicine increased, so did our use of it. More and more human afflictions began to fall into the category of "illness." Childbirth, aging, and death were suddenly seen as treatable conditions. Big Pharma and direct-to-consumer advertising normalized drug consumption and turned entire populations into medical consumers. The prime directive for every human affliction has become "see your doctor."

This shadow side of modern medicine was famously noted by Ivan Illich in his classic work *Medical Nemesis*. For Illich, modern medicine causes as much suffering as it cures. Most importantly, it disempowers the human animal. When every affliction is treated by some external substance or method, the body is no longer challenged to exercise its native powers of adaptability. And when these powers go unused, they go dormant. The end result is a population marked by weakness and the inability to adapt.

This leads us to some highly disorienting conclusions. We are accustomed to calling for more and better medical care for every human affliction, but in this light, we might well say that modern medicine is itself a threat to public health. We might even conclude that what the human body really needs at the moment is less medicine, not more.

Even when we do take action for health education and empowerment, much of our effort consists of little more than the generation and dissemination of information. We publish blogs, newsletters, and podcasts by the thousands, burying one another under mountains of health and medical advice. We now have terabytes of medical information at our fingertips. Never before have consumers had such access to the details of human physiology, anatomy, and pathology.

Unfortunately, most of that information is fragmented. Our knowledge of the body and human life has been digitized and categorized for easy manipulation and consumption. And in the process, we've completely lost sight of any underlying unity. As a result, our conventional health formulas seem inadequate, even irrelevant. We've all heard the boilerplate advice, the tips and "secrets" for a healthy life. Everyone knows the importance of a good diet, regular exercise, and all the rest, but many of us have grown tired of lifestyle prescriptions that don't seem to connect with any larger meanings.

Every day we hear about a treatment for this disease, a supplement for that condition, a test for this syndrome, a program for that ailment. Our health and fitness marketing has become a frenzy of random bits and *non sequiturs*. Nothing feels related to anything else. Magazine covers spew health advice at random: An exotic plant extract will stabilize your blood sugar, a needle in your earlobe will ease your pain, an insert in your shoe will cure your back pain, a probiotic will heal your gut, a fecal transplant will make you skinny, and an app on your phone will make you sleep at night. Likewise, a visit to the doctor usually gives us little more than a fragment of some unknown totality. We receive a substance, a procedure, or a recommendation, but there's no time for context, integration, or understanding. Almost never do we leave the office feeling whole.

Welcome to *The Art is Long*

Given the sheer wickedness of our predicament, many of us are inclined to despair. It all seems so insurmountable, so unapproachable, so final. The canary is screaming, but most of us feel powerless to do anything meaningful. Our problems are multi-layered and interlinked, with moving targets everywhere. Many of us can scarcely keep our heads above water as it is, much less take effective action to turn systems that seem pointed in all the wrong directions. We have no road maps, no experience and precious few people to guide us. Not only is Mother Culture failing to give us guidance, she often makes our problems worse.

And yet for all our woes, there's a promising fact hidden in plain view, right inside our very nature. As Yuval Noah Harari put it in *Sapiens: A Brief History of Humankind*, we are the most flexible cooperators on the planet. No other animal has this capability to such a degree. Chimps can cooperate flexibly, but not in large numbers. Insects can cooperate in large numbers, but not flexibly. As Harari tells it, the most pivotal feature of human history is our capacity to create and organize our lives around fictions. In other words, story.

Religions, myths, and legends are organizing stories. So too are ideas like justice, money, democracy, and capitalism. Culture itself is a constellation of stories that tell us about our relationships to each other, the earth, and the cosmos. Throughout history, millions of people have rallied around various stories and changed their behavior into new forms, for better or for worse. Stories drive our behavior, our culture and our futures.

The fact that we often use this capability for anti-planet and anti-social ends is beside the point. Without question, we use our unique gift in some spectacularly destructive ways. Stories that claim human superiority, profit over people, and unlimited growth set us in opposition to the very processes and forces that sustain us. But there's nothing inevitable about our current behavior. As flexible cooperators, we can organize ourselves around any kind of narrative. And if we can get the story right, better behavior should follow.

This is a book about seeing and acting on a bigger picture of health and the human experience. You might even call it a work of narrative medicine for the long body. It's not written to entertain, or even to inform, but to disrupt and revise our current frames of reference. By expanding our understanding of the body and the continuities that bind us to the living world, it offers an alternative to the dominant, often destructive narratives of our time.

In some ways, it's a new story. Modern discoveries about our bodies give us some powerful insights into the deep connections between *Homo sapiens*, habitat, tribe and culture. But it's also a very old story, one that honors the ancient, participatory experience of our native ancestors. In fact, the fundamentals of this story were in place a long time ago. Interdependence is one of the oldest of all human ideas. This is a story that sustained us for thousands of generations. In this sense, this book is also a remembering, a refresher course in who we are and how we can better relate to the world and one another.

This book is an answer to a simple, but rarely asked question: "How big is health?" If this seems an unlikely place to begin, that's because most of us think the answer is obvious: Health is as big as the person in question. It's synonymous with the welfare of the individual. It's about my body or your body. This reference point is the basis for our entire medical and fitness culture, but as we'll see, this "small health," "short body" orientation is inadequate to describe or treat the afflictions of the human body and life in the modern world.

In fact, our bodies are far bigger than they appear. Health is bigger than the welfare of individuals. It's bigger than most of what goes on inside the doctor's office or gym. It's bigger than the vast majority of marketing messages that we hear. In fact, health is as broad as our imagination. It includes the welfare of our cultures, our societies, our communities, and of course, our habitat. In a sense, it's as big as the entire world.

This book is designed to give you a fresh look at your body and the arts of activism. Along the way, it might even give you some ideas about how to be healthier. But let's be clear right at the outset: This is not a conventional health book. It won't tell you how to lose weight, grow muscle, attract a mate, or improve your athletic performance. It won't make promises of physical transformation or an extended lifespan. Likewise, you won't find much here about how to stop the clock of aging, heal your back pain, banish your arthritis, or cure your insomnia. You won't find exercise prescriptions, skin care tips, or recipes for every day of the week. There are mountains of books that will tell you all these things in great detail. In fact, this book isn't really about *you* at all. It's about us—the totality of our species, embedded in the biosphere. It's about our world and the long reach of our lives. It's about the bigger circle.

This is not to say that you won't benefit. On the contrary, adopting a big health orientation might very well improve your personal health and happiness. By taking the focus off yourself and getting back into contact with the life-supporting systems around you, you may well find new sources of strength, resilience, meaning, and purpose. Your pain might diminish. Your anxiety and depression might begin to lift. In fact, there's plenty of research to suggest the paradoxical idea that "bigger than self" orientations promote better personal health.

Even better, the rewards may go well beyond your physical body. By shifting our attention away from the self and onto our relationships with the world, the big health orientation promotes a more harmonious experience of being alive. By breaking down the distinctions between self and other, we move toward integration. By taking up the challenge of activism, you may well discover a renewed sense of meaning and relevance.

As you'll discover, this big health orientation is positive, life-affirming, inspirational, and powerfully humane. It shows us that we're not alone in the world, that we're deeply connected to history, culture, people, and habitat. In this way, big health is an antidote to so much of what ails us—our fragmented sense of reality, our isolation, anxiety, and depression.

Even better, you might well discover another side to the stress of mismatch. Living in an alien environment is obviously an epic challenge, but there's incredible energy here as well. The radical contrast between our ancient bodies and the modern world can be a powerful source of motivation for creative work. Our wildly improbable predicament is more than just a problem to be solved. It's also a potent driver of curiosity and imagination, a force that can move us to new works of art, as well as new behaviors.

As you'll see, this book is more than just a point of view. It's about taking action. It's about lighting the fierce green fire in your heart, inspiring you to make a difference. It's about becoming a warrior activist for our endangered world. Under normal circumstances, many of us would be content to talk about health as a standalone discipline, independent of large-scale policy and politics. But when we take a big-picture perspective, the call to action becomes clear. There must be a doing. In fact, there's a certain kind of beauty that come with this crisis. It forces us to focus. It moves us beyond the trivial annoyances of daily life. It crystallizes our thinking, our identity, and our sense of meaning. It draws us into battle and in the process, teaches us who we are.

Which brings us to our title. As you may have recognized, *The Art is Long* is a play on Hippocrates' legendary description of medical practice: *Ars longa, vita brevis*. "Life is short, the Art is long, opportunity fleeting, experience delusive, judgment difficult." In other words, there's an immense amount to learn and not much time to master it. Medicine is a deep, complex, multi-layered challenge that might well consume many lifetimes.

Our title also reminds us that human physicality and life experience are extended in space and time. Contrary to appearance, we are not separate, autonomous individuals. We are radically interconnected with the natural and social world. Appearances to the contrary, we live in a highly unified, integrated world. The body, in other words, is "long."

Likewise, *The Art is Long* reminds us that there is sustained, difficult work ahead. Learning to navigate mismatch is a challenging and sometimes arduous journey. The path to personal, social, and environmental health is often ambiguous. There will be no quick fix for ill health, lifestyle disease, or environmental destruction; this is a long game.

To that end, this is not an easy book. The ideas that you'll find here are disruptive to our familiar culture. The big health, long-body orientation will rearrange many of your most familiar categories of understanding. It may even lead you to a wholesale revision of your worldview. Even more challenging, it will call you to act on those realizations. You'll begin to ask more pointed questions about our medical culture, our education system, and the values of our culture as a whole. And once you're done, there will be no going back to a comfortable, small health perspective. Once your mind expands to include the totality of body–habitat–tribe–culture, you're going to be inspired to do something about it. Be prepared for some sustained work.

Big Pictures

There is urgency in coming to see the world as a web of interrelated processes of which are integral parts, so that all of our choices and actions have consequences for the world around us.

Whitehead, AN

A physician is obligated to consider more than a diseased organ, more than even the whole man—he must view the man in his world.

Harvey Williams Cushing
American neurosurgeon 1869–1939

To make sense of our predicament, it's essential that we adopt the right perspective. Every photographer knows the importance of focal length, and pays close attention to selecting just the right lens for the job. But as observers of the human condition, this is where we often get it wrong. We're deceived by the superficial appearance of the body, and even by our personal life experience. When we look in the mirror, we see a single person, a standalone organism, a "short body." We are fooled by the appearance of our individual selves.

The problem is that we're working with the wrong lens. Simply put, we are too zoomed in on the human body. Like amateur photographers, we're trying to make our way through the world with nothing more than a macro lens. We can get really close to flowers and rocks and other objects of interest, but the rest of the world is beyond us. We start with powerful optics, then tighten our focus with X-rays, MRI machines, CT scanners, PET scanners, and arthroscopes. We move ever closer to organs, cells, membranes, and molecules. We zoom in with entire disciplines: Anatomy examines and classifies body parts, physiology studies the chemical interactions between tissue and organs, histology examines the structure and function of tissues, and microbiology describes the workings of individual cells. Smaller and smaller we go, down to the level of membranes, organelles, replicator molecules, and even the characteristics of atoms and sub-atomic particles.

When practiced in moderation, this zooming in on the world is both useful and exciting. The small-scale details of the human body are fascinating, with entire landscapes revealing themselves in the structures of cells, synapses, membranes, proteins and hormones. The interior of the body is a wonderland; it's no surprise that many scientists spend their entire careers on the structure and function of exceedingly small component parts.

But as always, balance is vital. As they say in the world of toxicology, the dose makes the poison. Excessive zooming in ultimately compromises our vision and obscures essential features that are only visible from the panoramic perspective. To put it another way, we're suffering from a severe case of myopia. What we really need is a cultural eye exam.

Literally speaking, *myopia* is a condition known as near-sightedness or short-sightedness. The light that comes into the eye does not directly focus on the retina but in front of it, causing the image that one sees when looking at a distant object to be out of focus. The term myopia is Ancient Greek: from *myein* "to shut" (from *mys* "like a mole") and *ops* "eye, look, sight"—literally, "trying to see like a mole."

In March 2015, the journal *Nature* reported on "the myopia boom" and declared that "short-sightedness is reaching epidemic proportions." As more and more of us spend years and decades glued to electronic displays, our eyeballs actually change shape; the light that enters the eye focuses in front of the retina, causing the image that one sees when looking at a distant object to be out of focus.

But our literal myopia, bad as it is, is not the real problem. The thing that really threatens our future is our inability or unwillingness to see the big pictures of our bodies, our lives, and our societies. We are so busy zooming in on the details of our bodies and the world that we lose sight of the vital, panoramic ideas that might really help us survive.

The problem with compulsive zooming is that it makes us blind to other qualities and relationships. We come to resemble the test subjects in the classic "gorillas in our midst" experiment. In this study, researchers asked their subjects to record the number of passes made by a team of basketball players during the course of a game. It's all very straightforward, except for the fact that during the game, a man dressed in a gorilla suit walks onto the court in full view, thumps his chest and walks off. On completion of the test, researchers ask their subjects if they saw anything out of the ordinary. A substantial number of subjects reported seeing nothing unusual.

The same thing happens at the level of culture, compounded by our inclination to reward myopic specialization. Most of us are assigned tasks at some particular level of resolution, and we're expected to stay at that level, often for an entire career. We spend our working lives "counting passes." After a few years, we get really good at it, and we're rewarded for our efforts with honors, bonuses, and perks. We become successful, pass-watching specialists.

But along the way, we lose sight of everything that lies outside our immediate scope of interest. We become oblivious to the incessant destruction of habitat, the increasing fragmentation of society, and the yawning chasm between rich and poor. We're dedicated to our own level of resolution and we can only hope that someone, somewhere is looking at the bigger pictures.

Our relentless zooming in also leads to medical myopia. This is our hyperfocus on the individual, accompanied by deficient attention to life-supporting systems of habitat, tribe, and culture. We treat symptoms and syndromes with highly targeted therapies, procedures, and most especially, pharmaceuticals. It's almost unheard of for a physician to ask the patient about the larger relationships that sustain his or her life. We're quizzed about the nature of our symptoms, but no one ever asks, "How often do you get into the outdoors? How connected are you to your habitat and your community?"

This small health orientation occasionally works, but even when it succeeds, the side effects are substantial, even catastrophic. Every short body encounter leaves the patient with an increasing sense of isolation. The explanation for the patient's suffering usually hinges on some microscopic causal agent—a microbe or a virus, an offending tendon or ligament, or an insufficient level of a particular neurotransmitter. Rarely, if ever, does it connect to the larger, life-sustaining world.

Likewise, myopia has become a defining orientation of the health and fitness industry. Most trainers are nothing if not short body specialists. Corporate gyms pump up the individual with hard training and self-interest. Fitness marketing programs promise to maximize our individual welfare with all manner of programs, substances, and methods. This is precisely what we see in the world of health and fitness books, where the focus on *you* has become something of an industry in itself. A short list of popular titles includes:

You, Only Better
Health, Happiness and You
Kickstart a New You
You: The Owner's Manual
You: Staying Young
You: The Smart Patient

You: On a Diet
Nutrition and You
The Care and Keeping of You

And now, even being *you* isn't good enough. A series of self-improvement features in *New Scientist* magazine promises to help create a "Super You." And not to be outdone, there's *The Selfish Workout Guide: The No Gym, No Weights, Fail-Proof Way To Get The Body Of Your Dreams.*

The same myopic, zoomed-in perspective now appears on the cover of every health magazine. The human body is presented as an individual object, living alone, isolated and abstracted from its life-supporting systems of habitat and tribe. No background, no context, no environment. From what we see on magazine covers, we might well come to the conclusion that the body is perfectly capable of living in space.

Even worse, modern digital tools give us the power to manipulate the presentation for maximum effect. We take already-beautiful models and make them even more striking. We make their legs longer, their waists smaller, their muscles larger and their skin perfect. Hyper-skinny and hyper-muscular models tweak our sense of body image and, for many, lead to discontent and unhappiness.

The consequences of this zoomed-in, short body orientation are catastrophic. By many estimates, we live in what is probably the most individualistic, narcissistic culture in human history. We're groomed from birth to compete, perform, and excel. Humans are pitted against one another at every turn, and we live and die by our heavily padded resumes. Marketers are relentless

47

in pitching products and services to enhance and elevate the self. And as everyone knows, we've become a selfie culture. *New York Times* columnist David Brooks calls this era "The Big Me."

As Westerners, we're accustomed to thinking of this individualistic, short body orientation as "normal," and we scarcely ever stop to think in other terms. When things go wrong, we double down on individualism and personal ambition. But seen in the context of human history, our short body approach is distinctly abnormal. In general, native and indigenous people don't think this way. For most of human history, the tribe was primary.

Even worse, our myopic focus on the individual is actually a dangerous stressor. The deep human body wants to connect to habitat, tribe, and culture. Relationship is food. But when the body is isolated and attempts to live as a standalone organism, it begins to suffer. And this, as much as sugar, gluten, and trans fats, is a major source of our disease and unhappiness.

zooming out

Over the last few hundred years, we've become highly adept at getting closer to all manner of objects, organisms, and processes. Along the way, we've gained an immense amount of knowledge—but at a substantial cost. Our bodies and our world are fragmented and isolated almost beyond recognition. Clearly, it's time for a new perspective.

This is where we turn to the panoramic disciplines of earth history, biology, evolution, natural history, and deep ecology. Taken together, these fields force us to step backward, rewarding us with more expansive views of our bodies in relationship to the world. They serve as a powerful antidote to our myopia.

Zooming out inspires a powerful shift in perspective, psychology, and spirit. It reminds us of "the overview effect," a cognitive shift in awareness reported by many astronauts and cosmonauts while viewing the Earth from orbit. The story has become legendary: On Christmas Eve, 1968, the Apollo 8 spacecraft swept around the dark side of the moon. As Earth climbed above the horizon, astronaut Bill Anders pointed his camera out the window and captured one of the most important photos of all time, the earthrise. The term "overview effect" was coined by science writer Frank White, who explored the theme in his 1987 book *The Overview Effect: Space Exploration and Human Evolution*.

In light of our planetary-scale predicament and our radical interdependence, this must now be considered our new "reference perspective," a starting point for all of our investigations into the human predicament. By taking this long view, we see entire systems at work. We see relationship and interconnection and interdependence. We see human life in context. We see humanity *in vivo*.

meet the long body

Before going further, let's be clear about our definitions. First, the *short body* is simply the isolated, individual organism. It ends at the outermost layer of skin and has minimal connection with the so-called outside world. This is the body we see in the mirror. This is the body that appears on magazine covers, the body that we see on the anatomy chart in the doctor's office. This is the medical object.

In contrast, the *long body* is far more expansive. It's the totality of the short body plus its life-supporting systems of habitat, tribe, and culture. It includes the myriad plants, animals, people, microbes, memes, emotions, and ideas that flow through the larger system. It also includes the ancient history of our species, circulating in the collective unconscious. It is deep, wild, and powerful.

This long body view reminds us of the philosophy described by Aldo Leopold in *A Sand County Almanac*. "The land ethic simply enlarges the boundaries of the community to include soils, waters, plants, and animals, or collectively: the land." In our case, the long body orientation enlarges the boundaries of the human body to include the life-supporting systems of the biotic and human community.

But just how real is the long body? Is this just a metaphor, or is there concrete reality here? The answer is both. The long body *is* a powerful metaphor and a compelling story. But even if it were "just a metaphor," that would be plenty good enough. After all, metaphor has the power to transform personal lives and even entire cultures. Many of our behaviors and decisions are made under the influence of imagery, poetry, analogy, and other intangibles. If all we did were to promote the long body as metaphor, the effort would be plenty valuable in its own right.

But even better, there is concrete, scientific reality here. A substantial body of research demonstrates deep and influential continuities between the human body and the natural and social world. An increasing number of ecologists, neurobiologists, and systems theorists now point to the importance of human connection with habitat and tribe. As we'll see, interdependence is the law of the biosphere, and it applies to every species, including *Homo sapiens*.

The challenge is that many of the strands that connect us to the world are invisible in our routine sensory experience. Appearances deceive us. Just as the sun appears to circle the Earth, many of us believe we're walking through the world as independent individuals, a perception that's constantly promoted and reinforced by modern culture. Likewise, many of us are reluctant to accept the reality of something we can't see or feel directly.

But there's no reason to reject a connection or relationship merely because it's invisible to the naked eye. After all, we can't see bacteria or viruses, but most of us accept their reality and their power. We can't see DNA or the ebb and flow of hormones in our bodies. We can't see the microbiome, ultraviolet rays, or gravity. We can't see the activity of our brains, or the deep forces of history and culture. But all these things exist, and we would be fools to ignore them.

Skeptics will push back, of course. "How" they might ask, "can the body possibly be continuous with the larger world? How can remote events affect our health?" They want data, and most of all, they want a causal mechanism that explains the linkages between distant events and the health of the human body, mind, and spirit. Going further, they ask, "How can species extinctions, habitat destruction, or animal abuse possibly affect the state of our bodies? How can climate change, economic injustice, and the refugee crisis possibly affect human health across the planet?" For these skeptics, the burden of proof lies on those who claim continuity and interdependence.

But those who hold a big health, long body view wonder precisely the opposite. That is, "How can species extinctions, habitat destruction, and animal abuse *not* affect our bodies, minds, and spirits?" "How can climate change, economic injustice, and the refugee crisis *not* affect human health across the planet?" For long body advocates, the starting point is interdependence. The burden of proof lies with those who claim that human bodies are individual, independent units. It's up to them to make their case.

Interdependence has been a bedrock principle of human culture for the vast majority of our time on this Earth. It's been universal among our native and indigenous ancestors. And today, it's being validated by an impressive body of scientific research. It is safe to assume that our bodies are radically interconnected with the larger world unless proven otherwise.

Continuities

To understand biology is to understand that all life is linked to the Earth from which it came; it is to understand that the stream of life, flowing out of the dim past into the uncertain future, is in reality a unified force, though composed of an infinite number and variety of separate lives.

Rachel Carson

To your way of thinking, your skin is a thing which separates and protects you from the outside world. To my way of thinking, my skin is a thing which connects me and opens me to the outside world, which in any case is not the outside world.

Zen parable

As we zoom out for a big-picture view of the human experience, we begin to appreciate the true dimensions of the body and its reach into habitat, tribe, and culture. This is where we explore the story of our continuity and the myriad threads of connection, both literal and metaphorical, between our bodies and the larger world. The story has been told in many ways, by sages, mystics, tribal elders, and most recently, dedicated scientists. A selection from cultures around the world shows our universal interest in integration:

The Lakota people of North America say "mitakuye oyasin," a phrase that translates as "all my relatives" or "all my relations." It's a prayer of oneness with all forms of life: people, animals, birds, insects, trees, and plants, and even rocks, rivers, mountains, and valleys.

Carl Jung: "My self is not confined to my body. It extends into all the things I have made and all the things around me... Everything surrounding me is part of me."

John Muir "When we try to pick out anything by itself, we find it hitched to everything else in the universe. One fancies a heart like our own must be beating in every crystal and cell..."

Zen philosopher Alan Watts: "You and I are all as much continuous with the physical universe as a wave is continuous with the ocean."

Thich Nhat Hanh: "True self is non-self, the awareness that the self is made only of non-self elements. There's no separation between self and other, and everything is interconnected. Once you are aware of that you are no longer caught in the idea that you are a separate entity."

Zen master Yasutani Roshi (1885-1973): "The fundamental delusion of humanity is to suppose that I am here and you are out there."

And finally, John Steinbeck in his 1941 book *The Log from the Sea of Cortez:*

> And it is a strange thing that most of the feeling we call religious… is really the understanding and the attempt to say that man is related to the whole thing, related inextricably to all reality, known and unknowable. This is a simple thing to say, but the profound feeling of it made a Jesus, a St. Augustine, a St. Francis, a Roger Bacon, a Charles Darwin, and an Einstein. Each of them in his own tempo and with his own voice discovered and reaffirmed with astonishment the knowledge that all things are one thing and that one thing is all things—plankton, a shimmering phosphorescence on the sea and the spinning planets and an expanding universe, all bound together by the elastic string of time. It is advisable to look from the tide pool to the stars and then back to the tide pool again.

We've heard these all-is-one declarations many times, but many of us are quick to dismiss them as the musings of inspired, romantic, but unrealistic minds. And so we return to our daily lives mostly unaffected, our familiar perceptions and common-sense categories intact. One-world consciousness is for poets and dreamers, not normal people with busy lives.

But it turns out that these writers, mystics, and scientists were not just musing about some utopian, make-believe world. Their statements reflect not just an aspirational dream, but a biological, psychological, and spiritual truth. Today, a mountain of scientific research confirms the continuities between our bodies, our minds, our fellows, and our habitat. These are not separate, self-contained things. They are continuous with one another. We are kin with the world.

Continuity isn't just a curiosity. It's the stuff of sustenance. As leaves on a vast tree, we are utterly dependent on the branches, trunk, and roots. When we fail to appreciate our connection with the rest of creation, we leave ourselves isolated, vulnerable, anxious, and afraid. It is continuity that sustains us, just as much as food, water, and air. Continuity is life.

The story of our continuity begins long, long ago, somewhere in the deepest reaches of space. All the elements in the universe, including the very matter of our tissue and organs, came from the bodies of exploding supernova stars. As Carl Sagan famously put it, "All of the rocky and metallic material we stand on, the iron in our blood, the calcium in our teeth, the carbon in our genes were produced billions of years ago in the interior of a red giant star. We are made of star-stuff."

Our bodies are quite literally ancient; the atoms in our tissues are billions of years old. According to astrophysicists' calculations, as much as half of all the water on Earth may have come from interstellar gas. That means the moisture in our bodies may be millions of years older than the solar system itself. Every plant, animal, and microbe on this planet shares this same primordial origin. All living beings, from viruses to blue whales, are made of the same raw material.

No less amazing is the fact that all organisms on Earth share a common ancestry. We are not arbitrary, isolated creations, set down at random to populate the world. Our bodies are baked into the biosphere. As Charles Darwin showed us so elegantly, all life on Earth is intimately related. Like it or not, we are all kin: every human, every nonhuman animal, every plant, every insect, every microorganism. As individuals, we are simply the most recent leaves on an immense and ancient tree of life. That tree is our long body.

The story of our continuity emerges from the depths of evolutionary time. Our bodies are the result of billions of generations of adaptation—plants, animals, and microorganisms living and dying in intimate relationship with habitat and one another. Creatures that functioned well in habitat survived and passed their genes on to the next generation. Those that didn't became failed experiments. We—the current inhabitants of Earth—are the product of a multibillion-year program of co-evolution and fine-tuning.

The problem is that most of us simply aren't very good at understanding the depth of biological time. Humans just don't live very long. Our normal time-sense is built around our own short lifespans. For us, a hundred years feels like "a long time," but in the life of the biosphere, that's scarcely even a heartbeat. When someone tells us that life on this planet is three billion years old, we're likely to ignore it as just another large number. We just don't feel it.

But if we could appreciate the full depth of biological time and the incredibly tight interconnection between evolving bodies and evolving habitats, the continuities of the long body would become obvious. Of course our bodies are massively connected with habitat. How could it be otherwise? Evolution favors the forms that are most intimately connected to their world. Any species that was even slightly insensitive to the world around it would be in grave danger.

It's no surprise to discover that long, interconnected bodies are common in the natural world. Consider the humble fungus. A mushroom in the Blue Mountains of eastern Oregon is the largest fungal colony in the world, spanning 2,200 acres. It's estimated to be 2,400 years old, and the total weight of the colony may be as much as 605 tons. If considered as a single organism, this is the largest known organism in the world.

Pando is another notable long body organism, a clonal colony of a single male quaking aspen tree (*Populus tremuloides*), determined to be a single living organism by identical genetic markers. The tree-colony is assumed to have one massive underground root system and is estimated to weigh 6,600 tons, making it the heaviest known organism. The root system of Pando, at an estimated eighty thousand years old, is among the oldest known living organisms.

But it's not just fungi and tree colonies that exhibit long body characteristics. Entire forests show similar characteristics. In 2016, NPR's Radio Lab told the story of Suzanne Simard, a forestry professor University of British Columbia. One day, while digging a hole in the forest floor, she discovered a vast network of roots, completely invisible from above. This "forest underneath the forest" turned out to form a literal "underground economy" of nutrient exchange. By injecting radioactive gases into tree trunks, Simard was able to track the movement of substances between individual trees. Much to her astonishment, she discovered that different species of trees actually shared food underground.

Simard mapped the underground network and discovered that the biggest and oldest trees were the most highly connected. This "wood wide web" is mediated by fungi that trade minerals for sugar. Using this network, trees send nutrients to one another. Weak or injured trees pass carbon to neighboring trees, especially young trees of any species. Trees can also send chemical warning signals to one another. As Simard puts it, "the forest acts as an organism or superorganism."

We see long bodies or superorganisms in many domains of life: insects cooperate in colonies and swarms, fish school up, birds get together in flocks, ungulates travel in herds, dolphins organize themselves into pods, and dogs form packs. Of course, each of these species is unique, but we can be certain that they all gain some advantage by living and moving together. Traveling in flocks, herds, schools, and swarms, these creatures enjoy greater protection from predators, better foraging opportunities, and an increased efficiency in movement.

the earth connection

One of the most powerful continuities between human bodies and the world is our connection with habitat. Far more than just a pleasant appreciation for nature, this continuity is vital to our health and even our sanity. Every cell in the human body has an origin in the land, a relationship that reverberates across our life experience. When our relationship with habitat is strong, so too is our vitality.

The relationship begins with natural light. A flood of new research in the field of chronobiology shows how contact with natural light sets and resets master "clock cells" in the brain, which in turn set and synchronize thousands of cellular clocks that are distributed throughout the body. This synchronization is vital to orchestrating human and animal physiology. Without regular exposure to natural light, entire systems can become de-regulated, leading to disease and psycho-physical unhappiness.

Altered circadian and sleep timing has been associated with a host of health problems, including poor cognitive per-formance, mood disorders, diabetes, and obesity. But research from the University of Colorado Boulder, published in the jour-nal *Current Biology*, shows that as little as one weekend of camp-ing helped reset circadian rhythms and promote sleep. "These studies suggest that our internal clock responds strongly and quite rapidly to the natural light-dark cycle," says lead author and integrative physiology professor Kenneth Wright. Camping, we might say, is medicine.

Recent interest in this light–body connection is encourag-ing. More and more people are beginning to appreciate the role of natural light and taking action to keep their experience as real as possible. New apps on computers now adjust display colors to shift throughout the day: bluer during daylight hours and red-der at dawn and dusk. The International Dark Sky Association is doing good work in fighting against light pollution and register-ing dark sky places, parks, sanctuaries, and communities.

Nevertheless, challenges abound. It is now becoming obvious that our cultural habit of lighting up entire cities is a profoundly health-negative practice. Not only does light pollution disrupt our physiology and our sleep, it also disrupts nonhuman animals, birds, and entire ecosystems. Even worse, it deprives us of one of the most profound of all human experiences: gazing into a truly dark night sky. Today, a substantial percentage of humans never see the magnificence of the cosmos.

We are also bonded to habitat through our sense of touch. As children, we develop an understanding of habitat by direct contact: plants, soils, water, and animals. The experience literally shapes our brains. Neuroscientists increasingly talk about the hand–brain connection and the skin–brain connection. And in light of evolution, how could it be otherwise? The young body gets to know the world by contact, and we can be certain that the ancient human nervous system is most suited to sensing natural objects. We're really good at absorbing and comprehending the textures of tree bark, rock, water, and fur. In contrast, our touch experience in the modern world is impoverished. Surrounded by plastic and manufactured surfaces, most of what we touch is outside our normal, ancestral human experience. In this sense, it fails to nourish and sustain our bond to the natural world.

Food forms another bridge between the body and habitat. In normal human circumstances—which is to say, prehistory—all of our food came directly from hyper-local sources. We were intimate with the process. We hunted and gathered on foot, eating directly from the land itself. We had direct sensory knowledge of everything we consumed. Over countless generations, our physiology coevolved in tandem with the plants and animals of our habitat; we literally incorporated the land into our bodies. But it wasn't just substances that connected us to habitat. Almost every bite we consumed had some sort of story that went along with it, a story that connected individuals to the land itself. Food and story were the glue that bonded us to the world.

But powerful as they are, light, touch, and food are just the beginning. We also share an ancient and intimate relationship with the microbial world. Our bodies are home to vast populations of microorganisms that live in us and on us. Even though this microbiome is mostly invisible to the naked human eye, it is incredibly powerful in shaping our health and life experience. Microbial populations participate in a wide range of metabolic functions, including digestion and the production of neurotransmitters and vitamins. Some microbiologists have even described this population of non-self organisms as a "bacterial organ." Others have taken to describing the human body as a "superorganism."

The microbiome is a hot new area of research with great potential for curing disease and improving health, but the bigger message of this emerging field is philosophical and existential. The two million unique bacterial genes found in the microbiome dwarfs the twenty-three thousand genes in our own cells, which raises the question of who exactly is in control of our bodies and our lives. As Tom Insel, the director of the National Institute of Mental Health, put it, "This has enormous implications for the sense of self… We are, at least from the standpoint of DNA, more microbial than human."

The human body is, quite literally, a community. Some 90 percent of the protein-encoding cells in our body are microbes. We evolved with them in a symbiotic relationship, which raises the question of just who is occupying whom. "We are massively outnumbered," says Jeremy K. Nicholson, chairman of biological chemistry and head of the department of surgery and cancer at Imperial College London. Another researcher put it this way: "Don't look now, but the pronoun 'I' is becoming obsolete... Thinking of plants and animals, including humans, as autonomous individuals is a serious over-simplification." In other words, we are longer and more embedded than we appear.

This is precisely the point made by David George Haskell in an NPR commentary, "Life is the Network, Not the Self." As a biologist, Haskell marvels at the intricacy of a single leaf on a sugar maple tree and declares "This leaf is not what it seems." Looking deeper, he finds that each leaf is a community of fungus, bacteria, protist, alga, nematode, and plant:

> A 'maple' is not an individual made of plant cells, but a community of cells from many domains and kingdoms of life. Microbe-free plants likely do not exist in nature and, if they could be constructed, would quickly die for want of the vital connections that sustain life.

Much has been made about the wonders of the microbiome that populates the human body, but it's not just us. Every species is a composite of microbial and nonmicrobial life. The life processes of both plants and animals are radically networked. Plants, and animals too, are made of relationships.

For Haskell, "The fundamental unit of biology is not the "self," but the network. A maple tree is a plurality, its individuality a temporary manifestation of relationship." He calls us to expand our biological imagination: "When we gaze at a maple leaf, we now see not an individual made of plant cells, but a thrumming conversation, an embodied network. The "self" is a society."

We see a similar theme in the function of our immune systems. Most of us are accustomed to thinking of immunity in individual terms—as in, "I encountered a dangerous microbe, but my immune system destroyed the invader and all was well." But this turns out to be a misleading oversimplification. In fact, all of us are constantly engaged in a collective battle with the microbial world. Microbes are all around us, metabolizing and reproducing at incredible rates. If left unchecked, they would soon overwhelm us, but working together, our bodies mange to keep their populations under control.

What matters most in this effort is the function of the entire system, our "herd immunity." We all participate in this challenge. If one person's immunity is compromised, either by stress, disease, or a failure to vaccinate, others must make up the difference. If one person is a good germ fighter, everyone benefits. In this respect, our immunity does not lie exclusively within the bounds on an individual's skin. Rather, it is distributed across the tribe and the community. Immunity, in other words, is long.

Our continuity with habitat is far more than a matter of physiology or basic life-support. The connection goes deep into the human spirit. Many of us are profoundly moved and inspired by the natural world, a sensibility called *biophilia*. Not only do we enjoy nature; we actually identify with life and living processes. We seek out the natural world because it stimulates our sense of awe and wonder. We seek it out because we recognize it as normal. Nature is us.

Support for this human–habitat connection comes from studies of landscape preference. Subjects are presented with a variety of photographs of various landscapes, and not surprisingly, most people tend to prefer savanna environments and semi-wooded mosaic grasslands, especially if there is visible water and places of refuge. These landscapes offer the prospect of good hunting and gathering, ample range of sight, and easy walking. There can be no doubt that these kinds of scenes stimulate real changes in the human nervous system. Neurotransmitters surge and stimulate our interest. It's no surprise that real estate prices are the way they are; people are willing to pay top dollar to keep their bodies close to nature.

In contrast, it's safe to assume that we also suffer physical effects related to what we might call "landscape aversion." This has yet to be studied in detail, but there can be little doubt that the human nervous system rebels at the sight of urban sprawl, industrial domination of the land, factory farms, and clear-cut forests. Unlike the body-friendly scenes of the African grassland, these landscapes offer little in the way of refuge or the prospect for hunting and gathering. Our bodies and spirits recoil instantly; we don't need an explanation to know that something is desperately wrong. And we can be sure that constant exposure to these human-hostile scenes drives a stress response in the human animal. Our habitat hurts, and we hurt with it.

Our connection with habitat existed long before the birth of our species. Our primate ancestors had intimate, psycho-physical connections with the forests of Africa. A thousand generations of evolution fine-tuned their bodies to the plants, animals, soils, and climate around them. Habitat coursed through their blood. They knew their world in intimate, fine-grained detail.

The same body-habitat alliance is still at work today. In a normal human setting, children and young adults are quick to form bonds with their habitat, a phenomenon we now call "place attachment." The human nervous system, primed by a million years of evolution, readily soaks up the features of the natural world, mapping it to the brain and body. Until quite recently, this has been a universal human experience, common to every culture and people on Earth.

This attachment to place is still reflected in indigenous cultures everywhere. For native people, songs and stories aren't entertainment; they are vital bonds that connect people to the land. Culture is the glue that unites people with place. Almost every native culture tells a similar story of identification with habitat: "I am the land and the land is me." As the Yanomami of Brazil put it, "The environment is not separate from ourselves; we are inside it and it is inside us; we make it and it makes us." These people make no *self/other* distinction with habitat. The environment is not "out there." We are continuous with it. It is us.

Given this tendency to form human–habitat intimacy, it comes as no surprise to find that when this bond is severed, the outcome is catastrophic. We see the consequences in the experience of native people around the world. In every case, from North America to Africa and Australia, indigenous people who are driven off their land suffer incredible hardship. Entire cultures, built upon the human relationship to the natural world, have been destroyed. When people are displaced from their ancestral habitat, their primary reference point is lost, and along with it, the grounding for their bodies and their lives. When the long body is severed, so too is our contact with the source of life. Native Americans call this "the ancient grief."

From our modern point of view, we can see the displacement of native people and the trauma they've experienced with their loss of habitat. Many of us are beginning to understand the suffering that they endure: poverty, alcoholism, depression, and lifestyle disease in almost every aboriginal community. What we're less likely to appreciate is the fact that imperialist peoples also suffer the consequences of habitat dislocation. White Europeans left their homelands and conquered indigenous people around the world, but they also displaced themselves in the process. Living without a bond to habitat is stressful for every human race.

As we've seen, modern homes, vehicles, and workplaces are massively insulated from nature. Most of us have no meaningful contact with habitat. And even when we do get outdoors, it's usually arbitrary. Modern, high-speed transportation allows us to "parachute in" to whatever habitat we choose. We look around, go for a walk, take a few pictures, and go home. We don't spend enough time on the ground to connect in any meaningful way. We are merely spectators, not participants.

If we're affluent, we can survive this body–habitat disconnect. We can maintain our health, for a time. We can buffer the effects of habitat deprivation with exercise, distraction, drugs, and diversions. We can treat our anxiety, our depression, and our pain with various therapies and substances. But make no mistake: our predicament is similar to that of displaced native people. We too are isolated from the land. The only real difference is that we've done it to ourselves.

Of course, it would be obscene to equate the predicament of habitat-deprived white people with that of displaced native people around the world, but there are undeniable parallels. Western culture now enjoys the spoils of its domination, but we're also paying a heavy toll. Our lives may be comfortable with plentiful food, heat in the winter, and all the other conveniences, but we are just as isolated from the Earth as any displaced Australian, African, or Native American. We too are adrift and at risk. We all need a habitat to call home.

the social connection

No man lives within his own psychic sphere like a snail in its shell, separated from everybody else, but is connected with his fellow-men by his unconscious humanity.

Carl Jung

Just as our bodies are woven into habitat, they are also deeply intertwined with our tribes, communities, society, and culture. Once again, the continuity runs deep. Our drive to associate with one another is many millions of years old, sculpted by countless generations of adversity in the wild outdoors.

Prehistoric Africa was a dangerous place. As climate changed and the forests began to thin out, primates were forced to spend more time on open ground. Predators were everywhere, and early hominids were poorly equipped to fight back. Ganging up was the best option. By hanging together, we kept the carnivores at bay and found enough food to stay alive. It's no wonder that we are so intensely social. For most of our time on Earth, it was tribe that kept us alive. Likewise, it's no surprise to learn that our bodies are superbly wired to affiliate with one another.

In daily life, our social nature feels self-evident and not at all remarkable. We love talking to one another, and we spend most of our lives working with people and living together. If pressed, we might just say that we like talking and hanging out. But the thing we tend to overlook is the astonishing fact that our social nature is fundamentally physical. It's etched into the very tissue of our bodies and reflected in the deep structure and function of the our brains.

In *The Neuroscience of Human Relationships*, psychologist Louis Cozolino declares that "the brain is a social organ" and even goes so far to suggest that "there are no single human brains." We are so inherently social, so dependent on one another for our very cognition, it makes little sense to view brains in isolation from one another. Our intelligence, in other words, is distributed across our tribes and communities. Even without digital technology, we are massively networked.

Some critics say that Cozolino goes too far, but it may well be that he doesn't go far enough. After all, it's not just the brain that gets into the social act. We are constantly in communication with one another's postures, movements, facial expressions, and tone of voice. As hyper-social animals, bodies are paramount. In other words, the entire body must be considered a social organ. Vocalizations and language are just a supplement to our primal priorities.

Going further, Cozolino likens individual people to individual neurons. Like neurons, we are constantly exchanging information and communicating with one another; but even more to the point, we cannot live in isolation. Social activity is essential for brain function and general health. A neuron that is disconnected from its surrounding cells begins to die. A person that is cut off from its tribe may well suffer the same fate. This is why solitary confinement is now rightly considered a form of torture.

The story of our social continuity is also reflected in human attachment, particularly the bond that forms between infants and caregivers. This connection is a consequence of our deep history and our origins in a wild and often dangerous environment. As human brains began to grow, so too did the size of infants' heads. Naturally, this made for risky childbirth and high rates of child/mother mortality. Evolution solved this problem by favoring earlier births. More infants were born premature and completely helpless. Their only possible means of survival was to attach to a caregiver as soon as possible—usually Mom.

For the helpless, premature infant, social protection from the elements is absolutely essential for survival. Development to maturity will take years and in this respect, the tribe actually functions as a kind of external womb where the infant can continue his work of growing and learning. If attachment is successful and secure, the infant experiences the world as a friendly place and his body grows rapidly. His caregiver and tribe provide safety and nurturing, making for a safe home base from which the child and young adult could explore the world. But if the tribe fails to provide a womb-like environment, the child will experience stress and his development will be compromised.

In the Paleolithic, secure attachment was vital for survival. So too for the modern world. A solid body of research, beginning with British psychoanalyst John Bowlby, and validated by American psychologist Mary Ainsworth, demonstrates that secure attachment contributes to long-term success in health, relationships, and careers. It's a greater predictor of success than conventional measures such as IQ. And of course, insecure attachment goes the other way.

None of this should come as a surprise. For children, the primary relationship with a caregiver becomes the standard by which all other relationships in the world are judged. We generalize from our earliest experience. If Mom was reliable, nurturing and compassionate, so too is the Universe. If Mom was absent, hostile or bitter, we assume the worst and exercise vigilance, even hyper-vigilance. Early childhood experience set the trajectory for our bodies, our minds and our spirits.

Just as with habitat, we live and thrive by the bond. If either of these bonds is severed, we struggle. Our bodies retreat into fear, anxiety, and depression, and our health suffers. Our minds become preoccupied and fearful, our spirits become fragmented and incoherent. The tragedy of the modern world is that for many people, *both* bonds have been severed. Lacking a place and a person to attach to, many of us are now adrift.

Our social experience is far more than just an exchange of information; it's a highly physical act with roots that extend deep into the body. In fact, our social experience is mediated by an ancient, physical system called the resonance circuit. The system kicks into action when we observe other people's facial expressions, postures, and intentions. This stimulates the mirror neuron system in the brain's cortex. These neurons can stimulate physical movement, but they also fire when we observe the movements of people around us. This allows us to perform an internal simulation of what other bodies are feeling and doing.

Mirror neurons also help us learn fundamental movement patterns. That's why it's so important to observe skilled role models in athletics and dance. We observe and feel their movements, which we then attempt to duplicate. Once the mirror neurons are stimulated, descending pathways communicate with the deeper limbic system, the emotional center of the brain. From there, information travels deeper into the body via the vagus nerve, all the way into the gut, the enteric nervous system. More processing takes place and finally, the resulting information travels back up to the brain where it modifies circuits, particularly in the prefrontal cortex.

This understanding gives us a whole new perspective on our face-to-face conversations. When talking to one another in person, we're doing a lot more than simply exchanging symbolic language. We're actually sharing our bodies, our postures, our facial expressions, and even our gut instincts. In other words, conversation is a long behavior, a dance that includes two brains and two nervous systems. It's a physical, whole-body act.

Most of us have heard that the majority of human communication is nonverbal. We like to think that our words are running the show, but the body is always getting in on the act. The process is generally unconscious, but it's an extremely powerful force that's impossible to turn off. As job interview consultants sometimes put it, "Your body cannot *not* communicate."

We are incredibly adept at reading one another's faces and bodies. A study in the *Journal of Nonverbal Behavior* reported that study participants only had to watch about four seconds of basketball or table tennis games to recognize—from the looks on the athletes' faces—who was winning and who was losing. Participants were also able to quickly surmise whether the game was close or a blowout.

In fact, our bodies and behavior are massively influenced by a wide range of invisible forces, a process we might describe as "the invisible hand of neurobiology." This effect was vividly described by John Coates in his 2013 book *The Hour Between Dog and Wolf: How Risk Taking Transforms Us, Body and Mind.*

Coates traces the invisible biology behind fluctuations in economic markets. No one actually sees the biological changes that take place in traders' bodies as they buy, sell, and respond to market activity. But the flux and flow of hormones in their bodies are real and incredibly powerful. For Coates, market bubbles and crashes are driven not by economic theory, but by biochemistry. Increases in testosterone drive bull markets as increased risk taking leads to market bubbles. Cortisol on the other hand, makes traders more risk averse and more likely to sell, leading to market falls or crashes. Invisible, but measurable forces within the body shape our behavior and our decisions. We like to think we're in control, but visible forces are just the tip of an immensely powerful iceberg.

tribe or die

Given our intensely social nature, it should come as no surprise to learn that social isolation and loneliness are major risk factors for disease. As a predictor of early death, loneliness eclipses obesity, lack of exercise, and other familiar risk factors. John Cacioppo, a professor of psychology at the University of Chicago and director of the school's Center for Cognitive and Social Neuroscience, has studied loneliness since the 1990s. As he tells it, loneliness is an aversive signal much like thirst, hunger, or pain. Loneliness is unpleasant precisely because being isolated from the tribe is a life-threatening condition. If we lacked this aversive signal, we'd simply wander off into the bush and perish in short order.

Our extreme social sensitivity is even reflected in our sensitivity to pain. In a study reported in the journal *Evolution and Human Behavior*, researchers asked people to dance together in different conditions, some with synchronous movements, some without. They found that "Those who danced in synchrony experienced elevated pain thresholds, whereas those in the partial and asynchrony conditions experienced no analgesic effects." When we're feeling united, our bodies are stronger and more resilient.

None of this would come as a surprise to Sebastian Junger, author of the acclaimed 2016 book *Tribe*. As a war correspondent, Junger reported on the experience of veterans returning from wars in Iraq and Afghanistan and their attempts to reintegrate with society. In contrast to the highly supportive, tribal nature of their combat units, returning vets found themselves confronted with a hyper-individualistic American society, one that fails to provide basic human needs of contact, connection, and continuity.

Junger drives his point home with a little-known fact about white settlers during the colonization of North America. In that era, it was not unusual for white people to take up residence with natives, but movement in the opposite direction was almost unheard of. White people would sometimes "go native," but native people almost never "went white." For Junger, this suggests that there was something fundamentally humane about native culture, or something inhumane about white culture. In general, tribal living was more coherent, more egalitarian, and more relaxed than the rigid, hierarchical culture of white settlements. In short, the tribes offered a circle of interdependence that white culture did not.

Soldiers who fought in Iraq and Afghanistan suffered great hardships of war, but they fought as a unit with a strong sense of shared commitment. Life was hard, but the objectives were clear. In this kind of environment, soldiers had a sense of meaning and would readily die for one another. The war, right or wrong, gave them a sense of purpose. But on returning to the US, these soldiers were thrust into a world without a circle, without a shared sense of purpose. Instead of finding a community, they found indifference. Those who had suffered in war now suffered an even greater hardship: the return to a world where their contributions were largely unacknowledged and unappreciated. Gone was the sense of unit cohesion, of shared struggle and integration. Gone was the sense of *us*. In describing the condition of vets with PTSD, Junger challenges us to see the situation with fresh eyes. "The problem," he says, "is not with them. The problem is with us."

Knowing our history as hyper-social animals, it comes as no surprise to find that we would be highly sensitive to the "tribal vibe," even in our modern, predator-free world. Our legacy programming continues to run in the background and we remain vigilant for any sign of social inclusion or exclusion. Even the smallest social cues can impact our bodies and change our behavior. Indeed, our deep bodies remember the social imperative. When surrounded by a vast, dangerous habitat, it's "tribe or die." When we feel that we're included, our bodies relax and function better. But when we feel excluded, we lapse into a heightened sense of fear, anxiety, and vigilance. Ostracism feels like a kind of death, because in a way, it is.

ubuntu: "I am because we are"

For hyper-social animals, isolation is scary. When you're alone, you're exposed to the world, and your body knows it. Consciously or not, you feel your nakedness and your vulnerability. Lions and tigers and bears prowl the perimeters of our lives, keeping us on edge, driving us toward one another. Today, our ancient minds continue to feel the same anxieties, even when we're isolated in modern cities with swarms of people all around us. In fact, isolation may well be a defining disease of our time, and it's clearly bad for our health. According to some studies, living in isolation may be the equivalent of smoking fifteen cigarettes per day. Of course, everyone has different appetites for solitude and society, but in general, the human body needs other people to thrive and survive.

Given our history of exposure on the grassland of the Paleolithic era, it's no wonder that native Africans created a philosophy of social identity called "ubuntu." The word originates from a Bantu dialect and is pronounced as *uu-Boon-too*. According to ubuntu, there exists a common bond between all, and it is through this bond, through our interaction with our fellow human beings, that we discover our own human qualities.

A popular Nguni-language saying is "Umuntu Ngumuntu Ngabantu." In English, we say "We are people *through* other people." We affirm our humanity when we acknowledge that of others. Likewise, a translation offered by Liberian peace activist Leymah Gbowee says, "I am who I am because of who we are."

It's easy to imagine where this sense of social identity came from. Only a short time ago, human populations were small, and people were widely dispersed across the land. Without technology and infrastructure, people were totally dependent on their wits and one another to stay alive. There wasn't an option to go it alone. Predators were everywhere, and everyone depended on the tribe's oral tradition—the repository of knowledge about plants and animals—to get enough to eat. Modern notions of freedom and independence would have been considered strange, even unthinkable. Affiliation was what kept us alive.

It's no wonder that native people were so powerfully bonded. South African Nobel Laureate Archbishop Desmond Tutu describes ubuntu as

> ... the essence of being human. It speaks of the fact that my humanity is caught up and is inextricably bound up in yours. I am human because I belong. It speaks about wholeness, it speaks about compassion. A person with ubuntu is welcoming, hospitable, warm and generous, willing to share. Such people are open and available to others, willing to be vulnerable, affirming of others, do not feel threatened that others are able and good, for they have a proper self-assurance that comes from knowing that they belong in a greater whole. They know that they are diminished when others are humiliated, diminished when others are oppressed, diminished when others are treated as if they were less than who they are. The quality of Ubuntu gives people resilience, enabling them to survive and emerge still human despite all efforts to dehumanize them.

Ubuntu culture recognizes the intrinsic value of all people, regardless of their characteristics. It focuses on commonality, not difference: we are bound together by our universal human predicament, our encounter with the mystery and impermanence of life. In this sense, there are no "others." We are all of one tribe, one human family. This is a classic long body view.

And while the word *ubuntu* is sub-Saharan African, the concept is not unique to that region. Similar ideas of social identity and inclusion are common in most indigenous cultures. It's safe to say that every great society has embraced some kind of *ubuntu* philosophy. Of course, the modern world is often anti-*ubuntu*. Hierarchical systems and intense competition often force people apart. Technology, dwellings, vehicles, and expert professions often serve to separate us from our normal tribal inclinations. And once broken apart, we have a hard time finding our way back to one another.

Ubuntu sounds like a warm and comforting concept, but we might well wonder if the human brain is up to the task of radical social inclusion. Anthropologist Robin Dunbar has proposed that there's a cognitive limit to the number of people with whom we can maintain stable social relationships. By using the average human brain size and extrapolating from the results of other primates, he proposed that humans can comfortably maintain about 150 stable relationships. In other words, we're wired for the small-to-medium-sized tribes that were typical in prehistory. In this kind of social environment, we're fully capable of inclusivity, loyalty, and pro-social behavior.

But what happens when the human "tribe" numbers in the billions? In evolutionary and neurological terms, the challenge is completely unprecedented. We'd like to be fully inclusive and socially accepting, but it seems that our brains can only stretch so far. When faced with the prospect of welcoming millions and even billions into our circle, we balk and revert to primitive in-group/out-group distinctions, xenophobia, and warfare. We threaten to build walls and deport people who cross our borders.

Can we make the leap from small tribes to a vast, planetary mega-tribe? Can we teach ourselves to embrace a "big ubuntu" philosophy and way of life? It's the challenge of our time. We may not be wired to welcome seven billion people into our lives, but perhaps we can find a solution in our hearts. Can you approach the strangers in your life as full tribe members and allies in survival? It might feel like a stretch, especially in this age of polarization, but it is not impossible. Dunbar's number may be finite, but the moral imagination is not.

the social gradient of health

Given our hyper-social nature, it should come as no surprise to find that health and disease are closely related to our position in society. In conventional conversations, we're accustomed to thinking of disease in a strictly Newtonian, cause-and-effect model in which some particular agent or pathogen is the culprit. The thing that's making us sick is sugar or gluten or a renegade microbe.

But it turns out that disease can also be a function of rank in a social hierarchy. This fact became clear with the 2005 publication of *The Status Syndrome* by epidemiologist Michael Marmot. Marmot has compiled thirty years of evidence demonstrating the crucial importance of social rank in our health and well-being. His conclusion is that "health follows a social gradient."

In reviewing hundreds of studies from around the world, Marmot found that social inequalities are powerful determinants of human health: "Wherever we are in the social hierarchy, our health is likely to be better than those below us and worse than those above us." This holds true, not just for one particular kind of illness, but for all forms of human affliction. "Being low in the hierarchy means a greater susceptibility to just about every disease that's going."

Marmot spent almost three decades studying the health of British civil servants. His team followed thousands of civil servants, all classified according to their ranking in the occupational hierarchy. The findings showed a dramatic social gradient in mortality for most major causes of death: disease of the cardiovascular, renal, gastrointestinal, and respiratory systems, most cancers, accidental deaths and violent deaths. His conclusion was that "subtle differences in social ranking can lead to dramatic differences in health."

Marmot's findings have been confirmed by other research. In one study, researchers looked at seventy-two years of Academy Awards and discovered that award-winning actors and actresses lived four years longer than their costars and actors who were nominated but did not win. In another, researchers exposed a group of men to a cold virus, then placed them in quarantine to study their reaction. Participants filled out questionnaires designed to reveal the extent of their social relationships. The finding: people with few social ties had three times the incidence of colds compared to those with a rich set of social relationships.

This is where conventional health advice so often goes astray. Seduced by the apparent power of the short, biomedical model, we think that health is simply a matter of tweaking our medications, diet, and exercise formulas. But substances and formulas can never put us in the right relationship with anything, nor can they change our status in society. If we perceive ourselves to be of low rank, our health will be at risk no matter what we eat, drink or ingest.

The discovery of the social gradient in health is highly disruptive to medicine as usual. In conventional, modern circles, we talk as if health is strictly a personal matter, confined to the bodies of individuals. But in fact, health is a lot bigger than we thought. The state of our bodies and minds are intimately intertwined with large-scale matters of society and culture, equity, and even justice. The lesson is obvious: All of our efforts at high medicine-tech medicine, gene sequencing, artificial intelligence and robotic surgery, can never be a complete solution. We have to act at larger scales too. Ultimately, it's the integrity of the whole that matters. As early Buddhist teacher Vimalakirti put it, "If the people are sick, I too am sick; only when everyone is healthy will I too be healthy."

long cognition

Just as we begin to appreciate the continuities between human bodies, society and culture, we begin to see that even our minds are "long." Most of us like to imagine that we think with our own personal, private brains, but this is just an illusion. In fact, we are not the exclusive authors of our thoughts or our actions. Poet Gary Snyder put it this way in *The Practice of the Wild:*

> American society operates under the delusion that we are
> each a kind of "solitary knower"—that we exist as rootless
> intelligences without layers of localized contexts. Just a
> "self" and the "world." In this there is no real recognition
> that grandparents, place, grammar, pets, friends, lovers,
> children, tools, the poems and songs we remember, are
> what we *think with*. Such a solitary mind–if it could exist–
> would be a boring prisoner of abstractions.

We now know that the disembodied Cartesian mind is a fallacy. In fact, we think with everything around us. We think with our bodies and our physical movements, a process called embodied cognition. Our intelligence is more than formal operations on abstract symbols; it's something generated by our bodies. Here we're reminded of the sculptor Auguste Rodin and his famous work "The Thinker."

> What makes my Thinker think is that he thinks not only
> with his brain, with his knitted brow, his distended nostrils,
> and compressed lips, but with every muscle of his arms,
> back, and legs, with his clenched fist and gripping toes.

Many of us have heard the new findings: A heavy clipboard causes job interviewers to rate candidates as more "substantial." A hard-backed chair causes subjects to drive a harder bargain in a negotiation. Using your non-dominant hand for a few minutes can reverse right-hander's judgments of good and bad. Sitting up straight causes subjects to express more confidence in their ideas. But embodied cognition is actually an old idea. Henry David Thoreau put it this way in his Journal of 1840:

> I never feel that I am inspired unless my body is also. It too spurns a tame and commonplace life. They are fatally mistaken who think, while they strive with their minds, that they may suffer their bodies to stagnate in luxury or sloth. A man thinks as well through his legs and arms as his brain. We exaggerate the importance and exclusiveness of the headquarters.

Not only do we think with our bodies, we also think with habitat. The qualities of the natural and artificial world inevitably shape our ideas and our creations. Architects and interior designers know full well that people think and feel differently inside various structures. And of course, we experience radical differences in emotion and cognition whether we're indoors or outdoors. In fact, we might well speculate that the mass indoor migration of humanity over the last ten thousand years has driven much of our intellectual progress—as well as our sense of isolation.

My personal experience tells me that "indoor cognition" is radically different from "outdoor cognition." Indoor environments promote abstract thought, focused ideas, taxonomies, and categorization. This is where we excel at linear, executive work. Outdoor environments, on the other hand, promote relational, expansive ideas and fluidity of thought. When we're outdoors, we're less likely to be trapped in cognitive boxes, and more likely to be enchanted, inspired, and moved.

This indoor–outdoor distinction is bound to be a fertile area of cognitive research in coming years, but one thing seems certain. The transformation of human thought that we so desperately need will come from spending more time outdoors. Indoor cognition has run its course. We've had our fill of taxonomies, abstractions, categorization and spreadsheets. The next generation of powerful ideas will come to us in primal settings with open skies, natural landscapes and running water.

No matter how much we like to think of ourselves as unique, individual actors, our thinking is inevitably environmental and social. We are not the sole creators of our thoughts and ideas. Our minds and emotions are highly permeable to the memes and stories that circulate through the social bloodstream. Like it or not, our cognition is long.

To put it another way, our consciousness and intelligence is distributed. For our primal ancestors, mental activity was shared across the tribe as people hunted, gathered and explored together. In the modern world, we find a similar quality in the experience in sporting teams, mountain climbing parties, military patrols, and of course, love affairs. When people strive together toward a common goal, their senses, bodies, and behaviors tend to synchronize.

Naturally, this notion of shared intelligence reminds us of the collective unconscious, a concept made famous by the psychiatrist Carl Jung. In October, 1936, Jung described the collective unconscious this way:

> ...in addition to our immediate consciousness, which is of a thoroughly personal nature and which we believe to be the only empirical psyche, there exists a second psychic system of a collective, universal, and impersonal nature which is identical in all individuals. This collective unconscious does not develop individually but is inherited. It consists of pre-existent forms, the archetypes, which can only become conscious secondarily and which give definite form to certain psychic contents.

As individual thinkers, we like to believe that our minds simply came into being at birth or shortly thereafter. But for Jung, "The collective unconscious contains the whole spiritual heritage of mankind's evolution, born anew in the brain structure of every individual." The system is literally prehistoric. "Are we not carriers of the entire history of mankind? When a man is fifty years old, only one part of his being has existed for half a century. The other half may be millions of years old."

All humans share a common ancestry, have similar bodies, and, especially in the ancient past, similar life experiences. Naturally, our ideas tend to follow similar paths and embrace similar themes. No matter one's culture, race, or place of birth, most of us have some sense of mother, father, hunter, warrior, healer, earth, and sky. These are the archetypes, the raw material of our cognition and in turn, our culture.

As hyper-social animals, we're constantly sharing these human universals with one another. Emotion, gestures, postures, tone of voice, sharing, moving, shaping our experience, our relationships, and our ideas. This flow is powerful and deeply subterranean. It shapes our deepest inclinations, our fears, our desires, our sense of imagination and wonder. Our deeper minds are constantly in motion, together.

Just as our cognition is "long," so too is our intelligence and creativity. As ideas, observations and images flow through the collective unconscious, they help us devise solutions to life's challenges. We all share in the pulsing surge of energy that is the source of our creativity. Of course, many of us fail to see the continuity. For the last hundred years, we've behaved as if intelligence is a personal thing that's possessed solely by individuals. We test it, measure it and use the results to distribute opportunity. If you score high, we'll get you into to a better school. The rewards go to the rich.

But we are spectacularly wrong about this. In fact, our cognition and creativity are inevitably social and cultural. Our aptitudes are distributed across tribes and communities and now, across the entire planet. We think and create not just with our individual brains, but with our embedded social bodies. In this kind of environment, it makes little sense to say that one individual is more or less intelligent than anyone else. Of course there are variations between individuals, but what really matters is the collective intelligence and creativity of the group as a whole.

From this perspective, the widespread intelligence-testing movement of the 20th and 21st century now appears misguided. If intelligence resides in the whole, it makes little sense to evaluate the parts in isolation. What we ought to be doing is devising collaborative educational environments in which entire, multi-age classes of students are taught and evaluated collectively. Not only would this be truer to our tribal heritage and the long body; it would also be more in keeping with the way that teams actually function in the working world.

As for intelligence, so too for creativity. In conventional conversation, we're inclined to say that creativity is some special quality that's possessed by "gifted" individuals. We believe that the source of creativity lies within each person, and that if we can just nurture that capability with some kind of expert advice, we can be creative too. But it turns out that we've been asking the wrong questions. We long for inspiration, and we wonder where the great artists get their passion. We get blocked and frustrated with our inability to produce great content without effort. But our very bodies, minds, and spirits are themselves products of an epic creative explosion that's been pulsing, vibrating, and expanding for several billion years. We wonder, "How can I be creative?", but when we grasp the immensity of the long body world and the relentless generating power of the biosphere, the question becomes, "How can I possibly *not* be creative?"

The creative power of the biosphere is as old and powerful as life itself. It's astonishing in its diversity and richness. In every second, the biosphere is generating countless new individuals, new forms, and new combinations. We are literally embedded in an ancient, primordial creative process on a planetary scale. In fact, creativity is the normal state of affairs for life on Earth. But we forget this fact because we adapt to the familiar. We're lulled to sleep by our daily encounters. And we go blind to the awesome generating power that's around us and in us. Creativity is the water we swim in, and like fish, we take it for granted.

If creativity is the default state of the living world, why would any of us ever feel blocked? Shouldn't all of us be generating an explosion of art, painting, writing, sculpture, and music? This is where we can take inspiration directly from the long body. Creativity is blocked when we focus on ourselves, especially when we compare and compete. The more we see, feel, and promote our short self, the more we're isolated from the very source of creative energy. The blockage comes from our myopia, and our inability to see and feel the vitality of the world around us.

So get over the notion that creativity is some special aptitude that's only possessed by special people. Yes, some people do have astounding aptitudes—but this is a sideshow, not the main event. You, after all, are a creation yourself. So stop comparing and forge a creative alliance with the long body. Expose yourself to the immense creativity that is taking place in every moment. This is where the art resides.

Implications

In this great chain of causes and effects, no single fact can be considered in isolation.

Alexander von Humboldt
1769–1859

Prussian naturalist, influential to Charles Darwin, laid the foundation for biogeography

The first law of ecology is that everything is related to everything else.

Barry Commoner
The Closing Circle

Just as we grasp the true extent of the long body, we are simultaneously struck with a whole new set of ideas, questions, and conclusions about who we are and what we're doing in the world. Our big health orientation generates meanings that take us into new realms of thought, behavior, and activism. In the beginning, these implications trigger flashes of curiosity, but over time, they grow into more complete understandings and radical reorganizations of our attention, our values, and our behavior. And once we really understand the implications, there can be no going back. Our minds, once expanded to this new dimension, are forever changed.

it's all one body

Things get tricky right at the outset. Our big health orientation calls into question some of our most familiar categories and assumptions about our bodies and the world. Suddenly, we're confronted with the possibility that all of us—plants, animals, people and earth—belong in the same category. Our common distinctions between internal and external, self and other, us and them, begin to break down. We begin to see ourselves as part of a unitary, non-dual world. The whole world, as Shakespeare and John Muir liked to say, is kin.

At the same time, we come to the surprising conclusion that even this thing we call "the environment" is really a kind of fiction. It's a construct, a product of our language and culture. In the sense that it's something apart from us, there is no "environment." As Einstein would have put it, "the environment" is simply an optical delusion of our consciousness.

To put it in a historical context, we begin to realize that prior to the modern age, human beings didn't think of "the environment" as something "out there." More to the point, they didn't really think of "the environment" at all. This is a point driven home by Roderick Nash in his 1967 book *Wilderness and the American Mind*:

> Civilization created wilderness… Until there were domesticated animals it was impossible to distinguish them from wild ones. Until there were fenced fields and walled cities 'wilderness' had no meaning. Everything was simply habitat, which man shared with other creatures. Chief Standing Bear of the Oglala Sioux made this clear in reference to nineteenth-century contact with white civilization: "We did not think of the great open plains, the beautiful rolling hills and the winding streams with tangled growth as 'wild.' Only to the white man was nature a 'wilderness.'

Think back to deep prehistory, before the dawn of agriculture, cities, fences, and walls. Back then, we lived our lives almost completely outdoors, 24/7 in habitat. Life as we experienced it was all one thing. But when we built our first "indoors," we simultaneously created our first "outdoors." Inside implied outside. Tame animals implied wild animals. Suddenly, there was an "other" in human consciousness. Suddenly, there was "the environment."

From this perspective, it begins to look like conventional environmentalism may not be an ideal solution to our woes. Maybe it's just another face of our original problem. Maybe it's the sense of otherness and duality that's causing us so much the trouble in the first place. Perhaps we need to update our language and our orientation.

In the same vein, we're reminded of author Richard Louv's description of "nature deficit disorder." Louv recognizes our alienation from nature, but his choice of language is weak and conventional. His "nature deficit" and "Vitamin N" suggests that nature is something akin to a dietary supplement, something that we can purchase in a health food store and swallow with our morning coffee. Taken in the right doses, it will cure what ails us. We see a similar perspective in *The Nature Fix* by Florence Williams. If we can just incorporate this valuable "other" into our busy lives, we'll be "fixed." But these are unfortunate metaphors because they maintain the same "nature as other" relationship that's caused us so much trouble in the first place. They fail to address our need for fundamental, relational change.

Our language reveals the state of our relationship. In a dualistic world, we tell polluters, developers and timber barons to stop their activity because it's hurting "the environment." But maybe we'd do better to keep our eye on the unified totality. From this perspective, we don't say "Stop dumping that toxic waste into the atmosphere. You're hurting the environment." Instead we say, "Stop dumping that toxic waste into the atmosphere. You're hurting *us*." Dave Foreman, founder of Earth First! took these things personally:

Damn it, I am an animal! A living being of flesh and blood, storm and fury. The oceans of the Earth course through my veins, the winds of the sky fill my lungs, the very bedrock of the planet makes my bones. I am alive! When a chain saw

93

slices into the heartwood of a two-thousand year old Coast Redwood, it's slicing into my guts. When a bulldozer rips through the Amazon rain forest, it's ripping into my side. When a Japanese whaler fires an exploding harpoon into a great whale, my heart is blown to smithereens. I am the land, the land is me.

As our awareness of interdependence begins to sink in, we're struck by another curious thought. If everything in nature is intimately connected, where exactly do our bodies stop and habitat begin? We start to feel a palpable sense of continuity with forests, oceans, rivers, and grasslands. And in fact, these so-called "external" entities turn out to be just as vital to our survival as our so-called "vital" or "internal" organs. Zen philosopher Alan Watts put it this way:

> ...civilized human beings are alarmingly ignorant of the fact that they are continuous with their natural surroundings. It is as necessary to have air, water, plants, insects, birds, fish and mammals as it is to have brains, hearts, lungs and stomachs. The former are our external organs in the same way the latter are our internal organs.

Suddenly, we begin to see our surroundings in a completely new way. Instead of pointing to lakes and forests and mountains and talking like they're something outside and beyond us, we take a more inclusive approach. That landscape we're seeing is literally part of our body. Not only are the forests and rivers keeping me alive, they are literally part of me. As Wes Jackson, president of The Land Institute put it, "the planet is seamless."

So what then are we to make of the wholesale destruction of these "external organs" for profit? Now, instead of seeing environmental destruction simply as a regrettable event "out there," we come to the inescapable conclusion that destroying habitat for profit is very much akin to selling your own internal organs for cash. If this seems like a stretch, it may interest you to know that there is now a thriving "red market" for human organs. A substantial number of people are in fact selling their internal organs for profit. Kidneys, corneas, bone marrow, pieces of lung, liver and teeth; there are people out there who are willing to pay. Presumably, most of the donors are selling "dispensable organs" like blood and single kidneys, but these days, you never know what people are willing to do for money.

And this is exactly the point. As a culture, we seem to have no problem destroying the biosphere as long as someone is reaping a profit along the way. Today, almost every dimension of our experience has been monetized. Everything is commodity. Everything is for sale, including our personal bodies, our time, our dreams, the long body, and our future. And as long as the shareholders are happy, all is well.

Of course, you don't have to be a physician to know that selling, say, your liver, is going to have a substantial downside. Presumably, most of us would refrain from selling our own hearts or brains for a quick profit. But clear-cutting a rainforest or strip-mining the Alberta tar sands for a fast buck seems equally insane. It's all one body. You can only sell off pieces of it for so long before you wind up in intensive care or worse.

no self

This unified, big health view of body and habitat is just the beginning. One of the strangest and most disruptive consequences is that we also begin to question the self itself. The realization comes as a shock, then later, a kind of relief. In modern life, we are so attached to the self that we can hardly imagine that it might not be the central, defining feature of our existence. But the deeper we go into the world of interdependence, the smaller and less significant our individual selves become. We may even conclude that the self, far from being the core of who we are, is little more than a distraction. The self, we might conclude, is overrated.

In conventional, modern life, we listen to the voice of the self and take it seriously. We think, therefore we are. We pay close attention to our thoughts and our internal drama. The mind generates a narrative, and we accept that narrative as the voice of our personal identity, the voice of *me*. But in the long body, non-dual world, the voice of the self shrinks in significance. Now the mind is just a noise generator, a compulsive commentator on life's events, a strange and mostly unnecessary byproduct of evolution. We could almost do without it.

In fact, getting away from the self may well be an essential part of developing wisdom. Work by Igor Grossman at the Wisdom and Culture Lab at the University of Waterloo suggests that "self-distancing" can help individuals to make wiser choices. People who get outside of their own personal dramas are more likely to remain calm and optimistic. This is precisely what many meditation teachers advise us to do. Let the internal voice have its say, they teach, but keep letting it go. And as the self dissolves, it's replaced by the body and a sense of peace. No self means no adversary. No self means no noise. Let the deep body do what it does; selflessness is your real home.

you never know

It's not easy to get our modern minds around this selfless view of human experience and our interdependence with the rest of the biosphere. In fact, we may even begin to wonder about fundamental, red-meat issues such as free will, responsibility, and privacy. Many of our bedrock assumptions about human agency and behavior are suddenly open to question.

For example, life in a non-dual world means giving up the illusion that the self is exclusively in charge of our bodies and behavior. As we've seen, the human organism is always being influenced by society and culture, by forces of history, habitat and the activity of the microbiome. These long body forces are so powerful and pervasive that we might well come to the conclusion that our impression of personal free will is nothing more than a neurological magic trick.

Depending on your disposition, this realization is either terrifying or liberating. Most of us like to believe that we're in control of our lives, and research shows that even the perception of psychological control has powerful stress-reducing effects on the body. But if free will is nothing more than an illusion, then who or what is really driving the bus?

Perhaps you made an important decision today. Maybe you were proud of your conscious, rational calculation and the favorable outcome that you produced. But no matter how rational and intelligent you believe yourself to be, you can be certain that there were other forces at work. Maybe your judgment was swayed by the hot weather. Maybe it was the spicy food you ate and the neurotransmitters that were produced by your microbiome. Maybe your judgment was swayed by advertisements or world events. Maybe it was a memory that came up in conversation. Or maybe it was your back pain or the traffic jam that finally made up your mind. In a non-dual world, there's no way to know for sure. As hyper-social, ecologically embedded animals, we're always under some kind of influence.

This is not to say that we are nothing more than powerless particles drifting on the winds of social and environmental influence. We can and do make rational, intelligent calculations; sometimes our personal agency is strong, focused, and mostly independent. But let's not deceive ourselves. Even in our most rational moments, we are still immersed in larger wholes. We may feel like independent actors, but there's always more to the story.

Equally problematic is the issue of responsibility. Our entire culture of social conduct and criminal justice is built on the assumption of rational actors who are in fact capable of managing their deeds and behaviors. But if this assumption is flawed and people are always under the influence of the external world, what are we to say about the regulation of behavior? If human beings are constantly being swayed by social and environmental forces, how are we supposed to assign responsibility for individual action? Who exactly is responsible for the criminal act?

In this respect, the long body comes across as one monstrously perplexing idea, one that we're only just beginning to grapple with.

A similar problem arises with the issue of creative authorship and intellectual property. Who exactly wrote the book, the screenplay, or the lyrics to the song? Who gets to lay claim for the supposedly original idea? If we're honest, most of us can't really say with certainty whether our ideas are truly original or merely a variation on something that's already circulating through our culture.

We will not solve the puzzles of free will, responsibility and authorship within the pages of this book. Nevertheless, there's a valuable lesson here. Once we get past the notion that human beings are fully independent, rational actors, we're forced to conclude that some things about human behavior are fundamentally unknowable. In fact, we don't know why people behave the way they do. We like to present ourselves as conscious, rational agents with clear intentions, but mostly we are irrational animals who are under tremendous influence from elsewhere. It's impossible to tell the ultimate source of a person's motivation or the true reasons behind their action. We are all participants in the flux and flow of culture and habitat. Pure, unadulterated agency probably doesn't even exist, at least not for very long.

People do have some degree of agency and the power to stand apart from "external" influences, but not completely and not forever. Even when we think we are independent creatures of free will, we might well be playing out the influence of our microbiome, culture, friends, or the forces of history and world events. The life lesson is to give ourselves some slack. We do our best to accept responsibility and accountability, but the true story is always more complex than it looks. Compassion is the order of the day.

awe and humility

The long body view challenges our assumptions about free will, responsibility, and agency, but it also inspires a powerful sense of awe and wonder. Up to this point in life, our minds have been relatively comfortable within the scope of our individual physical dimensions. We've been trained almost from birth to see, feel, and experience ourselves as independent, standalone organisms. We are individuals, and the "outside world" is "other." The larger world is a curiosity and maybe a resource, but not much else.

But suddenly the doors to a larger reality are thrown wide open. Even our familiar physical dimensions begin to feel like an open question, and we suddenly become aware of the magnitude of influence that flows through our bodies and the biosphere. At any moment, billions of people are affecting and even sculpting each other's brains and nervous systems. All of us are participating in large-scale waves of immunity, psychology, and emotion. Billions of stories cascade through the larger human system, altering hormone levels, political inclinations, behavior, and susceptibility to disease. Minds are changing constantly, as culture is reinforced, modified, or rejected with each passing moment. Our hopes and dreams rise and fall continuously with current events. Once we understand the full dimensions of this process, we are struck with a sense of radical amazement.

The more we think about it, the more powerful our curiosity becomes. No longer anchored to our small, local world, we feel as if our imagination could take in the entire biosphere in a single act of perception. We can almost feel the totality of the oceans, mountains, plants, animals, and people, all participating in a planetary dance of interdependence. The great psychologist Carl Jung had just such an experience:

> At times I feel as if I am spread out over the landscape and inside things, and am myself living in every tree, in the splashing of the waves, in the clouds and the animals that come and go, in the procession of the seasons. There is nothing… with which I am not linked.

Some might describe this experience in religious terms, and for believers in a higher power, this may well feel familiar. But even for secular non-believers, appreciation of the long body leads to a similar sense of unity and even transcendence. Of course, biology and religion have long made for strange and even hostile bedfellows, mutually exclusive categories of explanation and experience. But seen from another perspective, we find a surprising unity. For those of us who are serious students of the depth and breadth of biological life, the insights are awe-inspiring and even, dare we say it, religious. As Darwin himself put it, "There is grandeur in this view of life." Grandeur, yes, and a mind-blowing sense that the biological world is deeper than we can possibly comprehend.

A corollary to this unitary, long body view is the realization that, for all our supposed power and passion, humans are actually pretty insignificant in the grand scheme of things. It's a hard message for some of us to accept, but it's simply unavoidable in this biological age. The tree of life is immense and ancient. The overwhelming majority of life on Earth has been and continues to be microscopic. If we step back far enough, humans begin to look like just another temporary animal.

No one likes to think of themselves as insignificant. Humans, particularly in the West, don't like to be humbled. So we push back on all of it—the big-picture views, biology, deep ecology, history, and anything else that would threaten our status. But while the message of long body biology may well be humbling, it is not humiliating. In fact, it puts us in the most wondrous company. Now we're in the same category as killer whales, elephants, bats, dinosaurs, and every other creature that has ever walked, swum, or flown above this gorgeous planet. This fact alone is radically amazing.

The beauty of biology is that it forces us to look into the familiar with what Rumi called "fresh eyes." Here we are, bodies made of stardust, perched on a small, spinning planet at the edge of a glorious galaxy in a universe some fourteen billion years old. Our bodies are home to an entire ecosystem of microorganisms. Our nervous system contains billions of cells, each with some ten thousand synapses, giving us an uncountable number of combinations of circuits and patterns. We are permeable to subtle social messages that flow through networks; not only are we breathing the same air, we are also sharing emotions, stories, memes, and ideas. And it's all in motion, all the time.

Many people describe radical amazement as a spiritual experience, which it most certainly is. But it also has profound effects on our minds and bodies. The experience of wonder sets in motion a whole cascade of beneficial effects that promote our health. Every time we see the world with curiosity and wonder, the body responds with a surge of health-promoting hormones and neurotransmitters. Our brains and bodies light up, increasing our capacity for amazement.

In *Awe: The Delights and Dangers of Our Eleventh Emotion*, neuropsychologist Paul Pearsall defines awe as an "overwhelming and bewildering sense of connection with a startling universe that is usually far beyond the narrow band of our consciousness." And not surprisingly, this nature-inspired awe is also good for our health. A landmark study by Jennifer E. Stellar and Neha John-Henderson found that "positive emotions, especially awe, are associated with lower levels of proinflammatory cytokines." In other words, putting ourselves in contact with nature's magnificence is really good for us.

The trick is to turn our minds around. Once we give up our dreams of isolation, power and domination, we can find a more comfortable way of being in this world. As Arne Næss, founder of the deep ecology movement has written, "The smaller we come to feel ourselves compared to the mountain, the nearer we come to participating in its greatness."

Of course, humility is not our usual style, and many of us lean towards hubris. In America, we sing, "This land is our land,"

and we're firmly dedicated to the idea of private property, resource extraction, ownership, development, and the cultivation of power. Our culture has "conquered" entire continents and peoples, and today we talk about conquering space as well. Most of us are dedicated human supremacists, committed to the notion that we are the alpha animal.

But from an indigenous point of view, this self-aggrandizing is outrageous, immature, and incredibly dangerous. For native people, humility in the face of the long world has long been considered a bedrock principle of culture, behavior, and survival. This wisdom was expressed in December 2016 at the Standing Rock celebration ceremony following the short-lived Lakota victory over the Dakota Access Pipeline. Chief Leonard Crow Dog described his people's struggle for preservation and their relationship to the world: "We do not own the land, the land owns us."

Throughout history, tribal elders have warned their hunters and their people against the dangers of hubris. Don't think too much of yourself or your powers. Just because you had a good hunt today doesn't mean you're on top of the world. Just because you found your way to water doesn't mean you won't be thirsty tomorrow. Be modest in your estimations, and save some of your power for when you really need it.

But of course, we see fit to ignore this ancient wisdom. We are in awe, not of the beauty of the cosmos, but of our own powers. We can do it all and have it all. There is no limit to what we can achieve and become. We can transform the face of the planet, revise the human genome, geoengineer the oceans and the atmosphere, and lay plans to terraform other worlds. Humility is for losers.

We even see it in our language, especially our sloganeering and objectives for action in the face of ecological crisis. A common refrain calls us to "Save the Earth!" But from a long body vantage point, this begins to sound like a stretch, even a delusion. We are one species, completely dependent on the biosphere for our lives. We aren't going to save the world. The Earth has its own powers, its own time, and its own path. And it will be here long after our extinction.

Our "save the world" language comes from a place of hubris, not humility. We talk like we are great cosmic rescuers, riding in on a big horse to save the planet. But this is just one more example of earth as "other." Only this time the Earth is not an adversary, but a damsel in distress.

So perhaps our rallying cries should be more modest. Instead of assuming a power position, we'd do better to advocate for something a little more in keeping with our position as a temporary visitor to this radically amazing world. "Ease the suffering of our habitat and one another" would be a good start. "Create better relationships with the world" would be another. These are things we can all do, no matter how small and insignificant we might be.

we are weird

As we immerse ourselves in the long body orientation, we find ourselves coming to grips with yet another disruptive conclusion. Suddenly, we begin to understand that our conventional, modern view of the world may actually be an aberration.

Until quite recently, all human cultures have been built on the concept of unity with the natural world. In fact, interdependence is one of our oldest ideas, one that's common to indigenous people in Australia, Africa, and North and South America. It's been our default view for the overwhelming majority of human history. It's only been in the last few hundred years that we've distanced ourselves from the world, a perspective marked by objectivity and non-participating consciousness.

From this historical standpoint, our obsessive focus on individuals, objects, and component parts begins to look strange, even deviant. To put it bluntly, we might even describe ourselves as weird—not weird in the usual, personal sense, but weird in an extraordinary, historical sense. Our Western scientific point of view, for all its power and value, may actually be abnormal.

This perspective has been famously described by authors Joseph Henrich, Steven Heine, and Ara Norenzayan from the Department of Psychology at the University of British Columbia, Vancouver. In their 2010 paper "The weirdest people in the world?", the authors question the widespread assumption that modern research subjects are representative of our species' characteristics and behavior:

> Behavioral scientists routinely publish broad claims about human psychology and behavior in the world's top journals based on samples drawn entirely from Western, Educated, Industrialized, Rich, and Democratic (WEIRD) societies. Researchers–often implicitly–assume that either there is

little variation across human populations, or that these "standard subjects" are as representative of the species as any other population. Are these assumptions justified? Here, our review of the comparative data base from across the behavioral sciences suggests both that there is substantial variability in experimental results across populations and that WEIRD subjects are particularly unusual compared with the rest of the species–frequent outliers. The domains reviewed include visual perception, fairness, cooperation, spatial reasoning, categorization and inferential induction, moral reasoning, reasoning styles, self-concepts and related motivations, and the heritability of IQ. *The findings suggest that members of WEIRD societies are among the least representative populations one could find for generalizing about humans...* Overall, these empirical patterns suggests [sic] that we need to be less cavalier in addressing questions of human nature on the basis of data drawn from this particularly thin, and rather unusual, slice of humanity.

The WEIRD paper was perhaps written somewhat in jest, but there can be no escaping the fact that as Westerners, we see the world in a highly unusual way. Our deviance is substantial and has significant downstream consequences. We have weird ideas about the body and health, weird ideas about habitat, and weird ideas about the role of the individual in society. We have weird ideas about time, progress, and change. Many people in native cultures think that we are, quite literally, crazy.

One of our weirdest ideas is the primacy of the mind over the body. As you may remember, the philosopher Rene Descartes was a dedicated skeptic who refused to believe anything that wasn't explicitly proven to him with actual, empirical data. After all, there might be some kind of evil demon pumping false information into his brain and how would he ever know? To be on the safe side, he proposed to doubt everything, *even the actual sensations from his own body.*

Descartes' skepticism was vital for the creation of modern science, and we can be grateful for his work. But on the other hand, this may well have been one of the weirdest and most abnormal ideas in human history. Descartes would have been laughed out of any native tribe, anywhere in the world. For indigenous people, physical sensation was vital, powerful, and essential for survival. In a hunter-gatherer setting, you don't doubt such sensations; you try to magnify them and listen to what they're telling you. This is how you stay alive.

But in the West, we took Descartes at his word, and now we're living with the consequences: a nasty mind–body split that causes no end of human suffering, an education system that gives priority to cognition over physicality, and a staggering epidemic of lifestyle disease that is sapping the vitality of people around the world. Our weirdness has given us great power, but it has also inflicted some terrible costs.

If you're wrong about the nature of the body, it stands to reason that you're going to be wrong about health as well, which is precisely where we stand today. We've spent the lion's share of our time and medical resources on isolated short bodies, while we miss the bigger picture of interdependence. But health is more than tissue and organs. It's more than the results of laboratory tests. It's as big as the Earth, maybe bigger.

We are so obsessed with the state of the short body that we miss the primal continuities that keep it alive and whole. Our conventional version of health, in other words, is radically incomplete. In fact, health isn't about all the usual suspects. It isn't about particular substances in particular combinations. It isn't about particular formulas for exercise, biomechanics, or training schedules. At its core, health is really about relationship.

It's about our relationships with our bodies, our food, our families, and our communities. It's about our relationship with habitat, culture, and our alien environment. And now more than ever, it's about our relationship with the planet and our role in making a difference.

new-old holism

There's yet another dimension to our weirdness. Our long body, big health orientation also wreaks havoc with our comfortable model of "holistic health." In conventional conversations, many of us simply default to the popular three-part model of "mind–body–spirit." We're happy to use this formula because it gets us beyond linear, reductionist models, and it feels more inclusive than the standard biomedical formula. We feel like we're opening up to a more compete totality.

But when we look at things from a long body view, we come to the conclusion that "mind–body–spirit" is inadequate to describe human health or guide us in choosing practices and treatment. In fact, it's not holistic at all. The problem, like so much in modern culture, is that it's laser-focused on the individual. Even worse, the mind–body–spirit meme has been co-opted by corporate culture as a marketing hook to sell a vast array of products from skin care and supplements to home furnishings and apparel. In this sense, it's even less holistic than we thought. But no matter how it's pitched, it's always about the individual. We might even say that this kind of "holism" is nothing more than reflection of our original myopia.

The good news is that some have proposed a more inclusive approach. In a landmark 1977 article in the journal *Science*, psychiatrist George L. Engel called for a new medical model. As a physician, Engel was disenchanted with the limitations of analytical biomedicine. He believed that clinicians must attend simultaneously to the biological, psychological, and social dimensions of illness. Engel challenged the reigning medical orthodoxy and called for the adoption of a more inclusive, systems-based approach. This became the known as the *biopsychosocial* model.

Engle did not deny that biomedical research had made important advances, but he criticized its narrow focus, especially its tendency to regard patients as medical objects with broken physical mechanisms. His approach struck a resonant chord with many, both inside and outside the medical community, but as we can now see, his perspective was also incomplete, something that native people would recognize immediately. Yes, bio, psycho and social elements are all well and good, but where is the land? Where is the Earth? Where is the thing that actually sustains us?

For indigenous people, this would be seen as a glaring omission, a rookie mistake. Yes, it's laudable that some segments of medical culture have moved beyond the mechanistic view of the body to include mind and society, but that was simply an obvious step in the right direction. If you're really serious about inclusion and bringing together all the influences on human health, you have to include the land. In this respect, even the biopsychosocial model is lacking.

We can do better. If Engel were alive today, he'd surely take a more expansive view of health. He'd spend some time with native people, explore their views on health, and reformulate his original model. This time he'd call it "geo-bio-psycho-social."

This formulation is more complete, but once again, it's highly inconvenient. Even if physicians managed to accept the notion that human health is somehow linked to habitat, how would that idea play out in practice? Exam and treatment rooms are famously sterile, as they should be, but so is the relationship. The encounter between physician and patient is scrubbed clean of any kind of "dirt" or "earth" that might interfere with the collection of data and the making of a diagnosis. The modern doctor opens a spreadsheet on his computer, logs relevant information into a text field and writes a prescription. The process is completely antiseptic. There's no time for habitat in the process. Sometimes even humanity is left behind.

Critics of a habitat-inclusive model would suggest that the Earth is simply irrelevant to human health. They see no connection between the land and the human body. They see the body *in vitro*, in glass, isolated from the world. The biosphere is simply a confounding variable to be eliminated. If we were to start opening up our medical models to habitat, we'd simply put ourselves on a slippery slope to irrationality. Better to keep the land outdoors where it belongs.

Going further, critics would tell us that the burden of proof lies with those who promote the health-habitat connection. If you're going to bring the Earth into the mix, you're going to have to prove it with a mountain of data, empirical studies, journal articles, conference presentations, and Nobel prizes. And if it fails to pass muster, well, so much the worse for the Earth.

But the case has already been made. It's been made by native people and by millions of years of evolution. Evolutionary biology tells the story in fine-grained detail. When a species co-evolves with an environment over the course of thousands of generations, it's inevitable that habitat and health will be linked. It would be truly bizarre if it were any other way.

Excluding the Earth from our holistic model and from medical practice is a radical act, and poor medical practice. To tear the body away from the Earth does harm to both. The agony of displaced people around the world is a case in point. So really, the burden of proof now lies squarely on the shoulders of those who would exclude the Earth and the land from their models and their practices. The evidence from native experience and evolutionary biology is overwhelming: if you want to say the Earth is irrelevant to human health, prove it. In the meantime, let's invite the Earth back into our lives.

rivers are people too

...everything has a right to be recognized and revered. Trees have tree rights, insects have insect rights, rivers have river rights, and mountains have mountain rights.

Thomas Berry
The Great Work

Interdependence is a cultural monkey wrench. Not only does it suggest new models for holistic health, it also forces us to reconsider our conventional categories that separate living and non-living entities. For most of us, it's a pretty rigid classification. People are living beings entitled to certain exclusive rights. Nonhuman animals might occasionally qualify as "living" and are therefore entitled to some measure of consideration, but these are exceptions to the conventional rule. For the most part, humans get the lion's share of the rights. We are the stars of the show; everyone else in the biosphere is there for our pleasure and utility. But when we adopt a long body orientation, all these categories are open to re-interpretation. When all bodies, creatures, and life-support systems are interdependent, where shall we draw our lines? Should we draw any lines at all?

The conventional line began to waver in 1975 with *Animal Liberation: A New Ethics for Our Treatment of Animals* by Australian philosopher Peter Singer. Singer argued that the interests of animals should be considered because of their ability to experience suffering. He also popularized the term "speciesism." In subsequent decades, the idea of animal rights has become increasingly popular. New discoveries in the biology of pain, coupled with revelations of widespread animal abuse in industry and agriculture, have led to a new sense of inclusion and a broadening of our familiar categories.

Similarly, the Nonhuman Rights Project (NhRP) is an American nonprofit that seeks to change the common law status of some nonhuman animals from mere "things," which lack the capacity to possess any legal right, to "persons," who possess such fundamental rights as bodily integrity and bodily liberty. The NhRP argues that nonhuman animals who are scientifically proven to be self-aware, autonomous beings, such as great apes, elephants, dolphins, and whales, should be recognized as legal persons under US common law, with the fundamental right to bodily liberty. This is an important step in the right direction.

The animal rights movement has generated a lot of interest and support in recent years, but the biggest potential change lies in what might be called the "habitat rights movement." The landmark ruling took place in July 2016, when a former national park in New Zealand was granted official "personhood." According to a report published by the *New York Times*,

> The unusual designations, something like the legal
> status that corporations possess, came out of agreements
> between New Zealand's government and Maori groups.
> The two sides have argued for years over guardianship of
> the country's natural features ... Chris Finlayson, New
> Zealand's attorney general, said the issue was resolved
> by taking the Maori mind-set into account. "In their
> worldview, 'I am the river and the river is me,'" he said.

"Their geographic region is part and parcel of who they are … The settlement is a profound alternative to the human presumption of sovereignty over the natural world," said Pita Sharples, who was the minister of Maori affairs when the law was passed."

Other countries are taking a similar habitat rights approach. In March, 2017, a high court in India declared the Ganga and Yamuna rivers to be living entities, bestowing on them the same legal rights as a person.

It's impossible to say if these actions indicate an enduring transformation in legal thought, but their symbolic power is undeniable. The act of granting personhood to a natural feature challenges us to do more of the same elsewhere. It also shows the absurdity of our conventional view of corporate power. That is, why is it that we are so willing to grant personhood to large corporate organizations, but so reluctant to grant the same status to the very land that sustains our life?

There is a deep absurdity in our conventional view. A corporation is considered a legal "person," with all the rights that go with that designation, but our habitat is a legal "thing." To put it another way, Exxon is a person, but the Missouri River is a thing. Monsanto is a person, but the topsoil and plants of the natural world are objects. From a native or indigenous point of view, this isn't just misguided; it is insanity. Obviously, our values are in serious need of adjustment. After all, our species has a proven ability to live without corporate power, but in no case have we been able to live without habitat.

There's another absurdity here. To describe a corporation as a "person" implies conscience and possibly even sapience. But the more accurate description is to say that the corporation is nothing more than a legal machine. It's an automation designed and operated for a single purpose: generating profit. Like a machine, it operates by a set of tightly prescribed rules for behavior. Deviations are not well tolerated.

Most importantly, the corporate machine must internalize profit while externalizing costs. If the company's product or service generates some kind of undesirable byproduct, it will attempt to shift that burden to the larger community, otherwise known as the commons: the water, the oceans, the atmosphere, or public health. If you're a fossil fuel company, you get paid for your product, but you let everyone else deal with climate change. If you're a food product company, you get paid for your food-like substances, but let everyone else deal with obesity, diabetes, and other disorders. If you're Big Pharma, you get paid for producing drugs, but you let everyone else deal with the side effects, addictions and disempowerment that come with medicalizing every dimension of modern human life.

To bring it all down to a personal level, imagine you've got a guest who comes to stay at your home for a few days. He uses your kitchen to prepares a lavish meal. He eats the meal—which is to say, he internalizes his profit. But his activity has generated a pile of dirty dishes, which he simply leaves in the sink for you to clean up later. In this act, he externalizes his cost. This is classic corporate behavior.

To be sure, the corporate machine does in fact produce some spectacular affluence, for a few, in the short term. But over time, it kills the life system that supports it. You can only leave your dishes in the sink for so long before the kitchen becomes completely unusable. You can only pump antibiotics and hormones into farm animals for so long before your customers become too sick to buy your meat. You can only pump carbon into the atmosphere for so long before the biosphere becomes uninhabitable.

Naturally, cynics will object that "rivers as people" designations will only lead us to a perilous slippery slope of habitat-inclusive thinking. Just imagine the chaos: If we grant rights to rivers and forests and lakes, this will simply open the floodgates to, well, treating habitat with respect and dignity. In turn, this could spell catastrophe for industry and the economy. But the thing we keep forgetting is that the economy is a subsystem of the larger and far more essential biospheric system. If the larger system fails, it doesn't matter what we do economically. But if we treat habitat as we treat ourselves, we can reap even greater rewards.

The writing on the wall is getting clearer every day. As more and more people take the big-picture, long body view, circles of expanding rights will continue to grow. Opposition is inevitable, but so too is the growth of our awareness. A vast body of research now shows conclusively that many nonhuman animals have basic emotions and feel pain. Of course they do. The only difference between "them" and "us" is a few letters of a genetic code. Most of what makes us human is shared across the entire animal kingdom.

Likewise, it's probably the case that even habitat can feel pain in some sense. We have no way to measure such a thing, but then again, what else are we to say about clear-cut forests and rivers that have been dammed? If the creatures of a habitat can feel pain, why not the land that gave them their lives in the first place? Isn't biodiversity itself an expression of vitality and flourishing? Isn't the drastic loss of biodiversity around the world a kind of pain in and of itself? I can certainly feel it. The very knowledge that the natural habitat of my youth is now covered with concrete and asphalt triggers my anxiety, despair, and insomnia. My habitat hurts, and I hurt with it.

It wasn't that long ago that we considered nonhuman animals to be entirely without feelings and therefore suitable for the most horrendous forms of experimentation and torture, all justified under the name of research. Today we know better. But future generations may well judge our current behavior in similar terms. It may take generations before we develop legal protection and rights for nonhuman animals, and corporations will push back hard against any consideration of "habitat as people." But there can be no stopping the narrative of interdependence or the expanding knowledge of biology. When you take a long body orientation, the rights of animals and habitat become obvious.

boomerangs and karma

Just as we realize the interdependent nature of our non-dual world, we're struck by the fact that our actions do not take place in isolation. Any time we act, we are acting on the whole and since we're part of the whole, our actions are always reflect upon us. Suddenly, we begin to see our behaviors in a new light. As our sense of duality dissolves, we begin to see that human behavior has a powerful tendency to circle back on itself. Whatever we do to the world, we do to ourselves.

We see examples of this karmic worldview throughout the indigenous tradition. Most obviously, we recall the legendary words of Chief Seattle (1786–1866): "What we do to the earth, we do to ourselves." In today's world, we would call this a great meme, but this is no mere one-off declaration of interdependence by a charismatic Native American. Across the planet, indigenous people have made similar observations for thousands of years. For these cultures, body and habitat were inseparable. As one aboriginal elder put it: "To wound the earth is to wound yourself, and if others are wounding the earth, they are wounding you."

Some may suggest that this kind of talk is exclusive to native traditions and is therefore irrelevant. But it's not just indigenous people who talk this way. In *The Meaning of Human Existence*, legendary biologist Edward O. Wilson wrote, "The human impact on biodiversity, to put the matter as briefly as possible, is an attack on ourselves." All of our behaviors, it seems, are boomerangs.

It's a common theme in many cultures. In the Eastern tradition, the Sanskrit word *karma* refers to the spiritual principle of cause and effect. It tells us that the intent and actions of an individual influence the future of that individual. Good intent and good deeds contribute to good karma and future happiness, while bad intent and bad deeds contribute to bad karma and future suffering. In popular conversation we say, "What goes around comes around."

Every religious tradition shares a similar "golden rule." Christianity teaches us that "We reap what we sow," and "Live by the sword, die by the sword." Likewise, "Do unto others as you would have them do unto you."

Of course, we are accustomed to thinking of karma and golden rules strictly in human terms. The "others" are people in our communities. But the time has come to update our notion of "others" to include habitat—plants, animals, soils, water, and atmosphere. Now we say, "Do unto the Earth as you would have the Earth do unto you." Or, as another modernized variation puts it, "Do unto those downstream as you would have those upstream do unto you."

This line of thinking sounds virtuous and healthy, but it also leads us to a disturbing conclusion. From a long body view, habitat is not just a passive, external resource to be exploited for human pleasure and wealth. It is a living organism, one that is vital for our personal health and welfare. In turn, we come to the inescapable conclusion that what we are doing to the natural world constitutes nothing so much as self-abusive behavior.

This statement may come as a shock. As a culture, we're getting better about recognizing, labeling, and sometimes even acting on various kinds of human-on-human abuse. We now recognize child abuse, spousal abuse, and elder abuse. We hear about physical abuse, sexual abuse, emotional abuse, verbal abuse, financial abuse, and spiritual abuse. And increasingly, we've come to recognize animal abuse.

But the term "habitat abuse" has yet to enter our lexicon; only a few hits show up on an internet search. But why are we are so behind on this obvious characterization? Habitat abuse is real, and it's extremely widespread. And it does real harm, not just to the habitat itself, but to all the people and animals that depend upon it. What else are we to call our relentless dam building, clear-cutting, strip mining, and development? What else are we to call the Alberta Tar Sands project, the largest industrial destruction of habitat on the planet? If habitat were a person, this is precisely what we'd call it.

Of course, the conventional reaction is to say that habitat is just a bunch of dirt, rocks, and plants, hardly something that deserves special treatment. But suppose that we were to remove an individual animal from its habitat and subject it to similar treatment. Most would agree to call that an act of animal abuse, so how is it somehow acceptable to demolish that animal's home? As it stands, we don't call it abuse at all. On the contrary, we call it "progress" or "economic development." When pressed, we say that we're "adding shareholder value" and stimulating the economy.

Speaking of habitat abuse, there's yet another metaphor that demands our attention. When we take the long body seriously, the rampant destruction of the natural world begins to resemble something very much like cannibalism. Beginning in the 1980s, a number of ecologists, including Paul Shepard, have been making this very point. In our relentless exploitation of the natural world, we are essentially consuming our own flesh.

In the conventional sense, cannibalism has been documented around the world, from Fiji to the Amazon Basin, the Congo, and among the Māori in New Zealand. Neanderthals are believed to have practiced cannibalism, and they may have been eaten by anatomically modern humans. It seems that we really aren't that shy about eating one another. As sophisticated moderns, we are quick to condemn the practice as "primitive" and "barbaric." But what are we to say about a culture that actively consumes the flesh of the earth itself? Is it really so much different? In a sense, we are eating ourselves alive.

When it comes to eating the very flesh of another human being, most of us consider the notion revolting. But we seem to have no such objections when it comes to consuming entire ecosystems. Perhaps if we thought of habitat as flesh, we'd have a different view of the matter. And why not? Habitat is just as sophisticated and subtle as human muscle tissue. It surges with life. A handful of soil alone throbs with the metabolism of thousands of species. It has a pulse of its own and is constantly engaged in a dance of anabolic and catabolic activity. Habitat is the source of our bodies, our food, our health, and our vitality. When we consume it, we consume ourselves.

Clearly, the time has come to call the thing by its right name. It's time to integrate "habitat abuse" into our lexicon and our criminal justice code. Most of us agree that child abuse, animal abuse, and spousal abuse are wrong. These behaviors are rightly criminalized. A long body culture would do no less.

rethinking the law of the land

While we're at it, the time has come to completely rework our understanding of criminal justice and criminal behavior. This is yet one more highly inconvenient challenge, but the dissonance is now impossible to ignore. As it stands, large-scale destruction of planetary systems is rarely considered criminal, but interfering with such destruction usually is. We endorse and sanction the exploitation of the natural world, but criminalize attempts to stop it. This is a complete inversion of long body priorities, and by that definition, an inversion of justice.

Examples abound. In December 2008, activist Tim DeChristopher protested a Bureau of Land Management oil and gas lease auction of 116 parcels of public land in Utah's Red Rock country by bidding on fourteen parcels of land (totaling 22,500 acres) for $1.8 million. No person or property was harmed, but DeChristopher was removed from the auction by federal agents and taken into custody, eventually serving twenty-one months in prison. In essence, DeChristopher was deemed a criminal by virtue of his efforts to protect land and atmosphere. In contrast, those who exploit and ultimately destroy the land and atmosphere are rewarded.

In October 2016, five climate activists closed safety valves on five pipelines carrying tar sands crude oil into the United States. This act of climate disobedience shut down 15 percent of US crude oil imports for nearly a day. The action was conducted with a high level of care, and the activists took extraordinary measures to ensure the safety of everyone involved. The only real damage was to a chain link fence. As of this writing, felony charges have been issued against at least one of the activists, who now faces thirty years in prison. In contrast, the companies responsible for the destruction of the Alberta ecosystem and the continued degradation of our atmosphere are rewarded for their behavior.

Obviously, the time has come to revise our criminal justice system with the long body in mind. Some questions demand our attention: Who are the real criminals? What constitutes a criminal act? What we call "criminal" is simply a reflection of our values as a people. It's easy to imagine that, if our values were reversed, so too would our definitions of criminal behavior. There's nothing absolute about it.

The whole point of having a legal system is to shape behavior—to punish, incarcerate, and possibly rehabilitate those who act against "the common good." Of course, we're accustomed to thinking of the common good exclusively in human terms, a fact that's reflected in courtrooms across the land. You can do almost anything you want to habitat, but any transgression against people or property will be dealt with harshly.

This bias against the long body is blatant, but what can possibly be done? Ideally, we'd write a new set of criminal justice reforms with the long body in mind. We'd set new standards for criminality that included "crimes against nature" and "crimes against the commons." The good news is that we're now seeing the emergence of a new paradigm of "earth jurisprudence." Inspired by the work of theologian Thomas Berry, this model identifies the anthropocentric bias of existing legal structures as it seeks more equitable remedies for both people and ecosystems.

The Center for Earth Jurisprudence is a team of lawyers working to advance law, policy, and governance systems aimed to legally protect the sustainability of life and health on Earth. Early successes are encouraging. The first law school course in Earth Jurisprudence was taught at Barry University School of Law in 2007. To date, over two dozen local communities in the US have granted legal standing to ecosystems.

Perhaps a new generation of legal scholars, judges, and legislators will take up the cause of earth jurisprudence, but in the meantime, there's nothing to prevent us from updating our language. You don't need to be a prosecutor or attorney general to call a crime by its real name. You don't need to file legal documents or hire an attorney to make a case in the court of public opinion. We can and should include such language in our normal discourse. As Confucius put it, "All wisdom lies in learning to call things by their right names." When you see something, say something.

environmentalism is health care

What we do to the world, we do to ourselves. What we do to habitat is what we do to our bodies. Habitat destruction is really a form of self-destruction. And of course, the inverse is also true. When we protect our habitats from destruction, we enhance the welfare and resilience of our bodies. In this sense, environmentalism is best described as a form of health care.

Naturally, this is yet another disruption to convention. We are accustomed to thinking and acting within familiar categories. Environmental activism and health care are said to exist in entirely different worlds, separated by miles of empty space. Nonprofit organizations attempt to save habitat while hospitals attempt to save human lives. But almost never do these two domains work together. It is unheard of, for example, for a hospital chain or physician's organization to endorse habitat protection as a health policy objective.

To be sure, the advocacy group Physicians for Social Responsibility is doing good work in this area. This physician-led organization works to protect the public from the threats of nuclear proliferation, climate change, and environmental toxins. PSR's fifty thousand members, activists and staff form a nationwide network that target threats to global survival. It's a start, but there's much more to be done. The division of body and world isn't just arbitrary and false—it's actually destructive. As long as we behave as if the human body lives in its own separate reality, our health is going to be compromised.

Likewise, we also feel the call to reconsider the roles of government institutions. For example, most of us are inclined to think of the Environmental Protection Agency exclusively in environmental terms. They're doing good work, but it's work about things that are "out there" and separate from us. But in a long body world, we see the EPA as a health care agency, only at a somewhat different scale. In fact, EPA scientists who study air pollution, climate change, and toxics have made this very point.

Some will protest that such reworking of big institutions and their missions would be impractical and inconvenient, but what's the alternative? To pretend that personal health and environmental health have nothing to do with one another? In itself, living with such an illusion is a dangerous and profoundly health-negative act. We defend these conventional categories at our peril.

language misleads

Just as we grasp the depth and immensity of the long body, we also become suspicious of the words we use to describe the state of our lives and the world. The long body is vast and dynamic, but in comparison, our words seem weak and even inappropriate. There's something about language itself that seems to obscure our understanding of the long body.

It's easy to forget that literacy itself is a brand-new invention. In the context of human history, the written word is a novelty, possibly even an abnormality. Historians tell us that writing first appeared some five thousand years ago, but reading and writing didn't become commonplace until Gutenberg's printing press and moveable type in 1439. Even then, our mental environment didn't become flooded with language until quite recently. For the vast majority of human experience, our primary exposure to language has been through the oral tradition.

In fact, the status quo for human experience has been illiteracy. Our primal "language" was the language of habitat, plants, animals, and human bodies. And if you care to include our non-human ancestors in the mix, the picture becomes even more pronounced. The vast, overwhelming majority of creatures in the biosphere learn and know the world not through words, but through sensation and experience. In other words, we know the long body through our physicality. Words are a supplement, even a distraction.

But today, we are drowning in language. Words are everywhere, flooding our eyes and our ears, all day, every day. We go to meetings and talk. We read and scroll, swipe and scan. We listen to news and talk radio, to podcasts and audio books. It's impossible to calculate, but it's safe to assume that today's human consumes thousands of times more language than our typical, pre-literate ancestor. The language centers of our brains are working overtime while our bodies and our senses atrophy. It's no surprise that we often fail to sense the long body.

Language can mislead us at a deep level. The classic rookie mistake is to confuse the map with the territory, the word with the thing. Symbols are not reality, but they are magical in their own way and extremely seductive. We are captivated by their power and their ability to tell a story. Little by little, they take over our consciousness and our attention in what Stuart Chase called "a tyranny of words."

Spoken words have their power, but they fade away in short order. In contrast, written words are like shards of granite, frozen representations of an inherently dynamic reality. We use them in our attempt to capture experience, but life moves on at its own pace, in its own time. The biosphere cares nothing for the words we throw at it. As soon as a word escapes our lips or is frozen by our keyboard, it becomes obsolete.

The biggest problem is the word *is*. We use it reflexively and without awareness, but its effects are profound and often destructive. This simple word flash-freezes reality, and in the process, leads us to presume a world of things. Every time we utter a noun, we isolate the thing in question and turn it into an object.

It's an easy trap to fall into. In childhood, we're presented with a series of static things that we're expected to identify and name: toys, balls, and stuffed animals. With this kind of training, it's easy to come to the conclusion that our entire world consists of nothing more than individual objects, separate and apart from one another. It's no wonder that we treat the environment and other people as things to be manipulated.

Western languages may be particularly suspect in this regard. Our conventional sentence construction of subject–verb–object sets up an expectation and leads us to believe that the world is composed primarily of objects that act upon one another. Our language makes it easy to atomize the world, to fragment it, manipulate it, and control it. Perhaps it's no wonder that English-speaking people have come to dominate the biosphere. It's easy to exploit the world when you think that it's nothing more than a box of things.

Static nouns are bad enough, but the real problem with language is the way that it sets us up for dualizing our experience and the world around us. The words we use often imply their opposites. Every time we open our mouths or put our fingers to the keyboard, we run the risk of driving a wedge into the world and our experience. For the dualistic mind, things in life are either black or white, good or evil, true or false. The dualist puts everything in a pigeon hole. If there's a protagonist, there must be an antagonist. Humans go in one pigeon hole, animals in another, and the environment in yet another. There is no overlap between categories, no middle ground and no interdependence. Obviously, this interferes with our ability to see, feel and experience the long body. In effect, it chops the long body into pieces.

It is not clear where black-and-white thinking first took shape in the human mind. Legendary zoologist Stephen Jay Gould liked to describe the human mind as a "dichotimizing machine." Some observers pin the blame squarely on Aristotle and his "law of the excluded middle." In this scheme, a thing must be either *A* or *not-A*. This rational framework paved the way for modern, logical thought, but it also set us up for unnecessary conflict and misunderstanding. In contrast, native people have no problem with the proposition that a thing can be *both A and not-A*. This is simply the way of the world.

Like all edge tools, dualistic thinking can be useful. When wielded carefully, it can help us organize our knowledge and solve practical problems. But the edge of dualistic thought does not serve us well in our attempt to appreciate the long body; many things in this incredibly rich universe simply do not fall into neat, crisp categories. Most of the really interesting things in our lives span a continuum: degrees of conflict and harmony, sickness and health, victory and defeat, success and failure. By seeing things only in black and white, we miss the fantastic range of color available to us.

Even worse, we find it impossible to entertain opposing ideas at the same time. We come to believe that we can be either strong or sensitive, but not both. We can exercise either brains or brawn, but not both. We find it hard to imagine something that is hard–soft or strong–weak. Yet a union of complementary opposites is precisely what the warrior activist needs to be effective. He must learn to distrust the common dualities: internal–external, self–other, inside–outside.

The long body is a unitary organism with both–and qualities. That is, she has qualities that lie on both sides of whatever edge our human minds might happen to apply to her. She is both fast and slow, conservative and innovative, comforting and terrifying, inspiring and heartbreaking. Nature never heard of Aristotle, and thus, a thing can be both *A* and *not-A*. Nature refuses to be pigeonholed, and laughs at our pathetic attempts to do so. In a long body world, it's relationships that really count. Objects might be nothing more than a distraction, even an illusion. As Ernest Callenbach put it in his 1975 book *Ecotopia*, "We don't think in terms of 'things,' there's no such thing as a thing."

For better or for worse, it seems unlikely that we could ever capture the immensity of the long body in any kind of language or any string of words. There's just too much going on. Even the complexity of a single cell at a single moment in time, is too much to get our words around. Trying to describe the intricacies of, say, protein synthesis or cell metabolism in detail would require thousands of pages, to say nothing of the rest of the body and its relationships with society and environment. Even our best words would be nothing more than explanatory blips in a universe of fluid complexity.

Fluency can make up for some of these linguistic traps. If we're adept at moving around the language, we're less likely to freeze the world or chop it up into false dualities. So yes, a large vocabulary and lots of practice might well prevent some of our most egregious errors. Hardcore practice with writing and public speaking will serve the warrior well.

What words can do is jump-start our awareness. They can prime the pump of the mind and lead it into some kind of awakening. Words may well be crude tools for exploring the long body, but they can also inspire our curiosity and wonder. Just remember: taxonomy should be a means, not an end to thought. Categories and pigeonholes are useful, but they may also lead us astray. Even pigeons spend most of their time out flying around.

politics are inevitable

One of the penalties for refusing to participate in politics is that you end up being governed by your inferiors.

Plato

As we grasp the true dimensions of the long body, we feel compelled to act. We realize that health is about a lot more than the state of our personal, short bodies. It's about more than sets, reps, and mileage, protein, carbs, and body fat percentages. What happens to habitat and tribe inevitably affects our bodies. And if we want to act on behalf of our health, we must also act on behalf of the world that sustains us. Our actions must be, in one way or another, political.

Sadly, this orientation is almost completely absent from conventional discussions of medicine and the body. To be sure, there's plenty of conversation about the merits of medical technology, food pyramids, the Affordable Care Act, and the safety of various drugs. But in general, the primary concern of the health and medical community is the short, isolated body.

Even worse, our interest in health and fitness sometimes functions as a retreat from the messy world of action. We've had our fill of the shouting, complaining, and jockeying for power, so we give up and head for the gym, the studio, or the athletic field. Here at least is something pure, something we can sink our teeth into without danger of being demonized for what we believe or don't believe.

It's completely understandable, but for better or worse, such a retreat can only be a temporary refuge. There's just too much at stake, and too much to be done. The very habitability of the biosphere hangs in the balance. And besides, there can be no real escape from politics anyway. Declaring neutrality is itself a political statement, a vote for the status quo. There simply is no place to hide. The body is inevitably connected to habitat and community. Health is *always* political. As the saying goes, you may not be interested in politics, but politics are definitely interested in you.

The problem is that most of us are conflict-avoidant. Being politically active means exposure, risk, and stress. So we avoid the whole mess whenever possible. If pressed, we rationalize our behavior and justify our nonparticipation. We tell ourselves and our friends that the whole system is corrupt, that it's all dominated by big money, and that one person can't make a difference anyway. So we offer up a few complaints about the state of the world and return to our careers, our bodies, and our families.

But it never works. Avoidance protects us from exposure, but in the long term, our inaction strips our lives of meaning. As inactivists, we are nothing more than spectators in the dramas that are unfolding around the world. Other people are fighting epic battles against tyranny, injustice, and habitat destruction, but we can only loathe or cheer, depending on which way the wind is blowing. In the end, the fighters at least wind up with a sense of purpose, while the inactivists are left with nothing.

A mountain of evidence now points to the power of purpose and meaning in health. Famously, this exploration began with Viktor Frankl and his classic work *Man's Search for Meaning*. Frankl was a psychotherapist who was taken prisoner in the Second World War, spending several years in various prison camps, including Auschwitz. As Frankl observed his fellow inmates and their responses to almost unimaginable levels of stress and suffering, he concluded that it was the prisoner's ability to connect with meaning that made the difference in their survival. Frankl often quoted Nietzsche: "He who has a *why* to live can endure almost any *how*."

We hear a similar theme in Kelly McGonigal's *The Upside of Stress: Why Stress is Good for You and How to Get Good at It*. For McGonigal, stress is not an enemy, but rather a natural byproduct of a purposeful, meaningful life. And in this sense, stress isn't something to be avoided or defeated. It's a sign that you're on the right track.

Obviously, there's plenty to be depressed about in the world of politics these days, and a million reasons not to be engaged. But the bigger risk may well be nonengagement. By removing ourselves from the field of political battle and retreating into our personal lives, we risk more than we think. Our failure to engage ultimately saps our energy and leaves us vulnerable to depression. Without something to fight for or against, we lapse into a shallow life. The comfort feels good for a time, but ultimately, it becomes its own kind of poison.

Fortunately, we have plenty to fight for today. The long body desperately needs us, and the fight is therapeutic. Win or lose, engaging the battle is actually a powerful path to health, just as important as going to the gym, the track, or the dojo. You may not get sweaty, and you may even lose some battles, but the engagement will make you stronger. This is the province—the sacrifice and the payoff—of the warrior activist.

The Warrior Activist

It's time for a warrior society to rise up out of the Earth and throw itself in front of the juggernaut of destruction.

Dave Foreman

Find your place on the planet. Dig in, and take responsibility from there.

Gary Snyder

The long body is in trouble. No matter where we look, environmental and social continuities are stressed to the limit. The problems of the day feel overwhelming, intimidating, and complex beyond our imagination. For many, just making it through a typical day is challenge enough.

When we do engage in activism, we find the process frustrating and exhausting. Earth-hostile forces are extremely powerful and resistant to change. Access to the halls of government is restricted to the wealthy and the already powerful. Arcane rules of administration seem incomprehensible. People are distracted and impossible to pin down. Emails seem to go nowhere, phone calls go unreturned. Battles are usually protracted, and defeat is common. In this effort, the spirit of the activist is tested deeply and repeatedly. Without a unifying idea or image to draw on, the activist runs the risk of falling into despair and resignation.

This is why the warrior archetype is so vital. The warrior spirit is timeless and universal. It engages our moral and physical imagination. It puts us in good company, united with all those courageous individuals who have gone before us, fighting great battles against incredible odds. It reminds us of our inherent resilience and capacity for extraordinary efforts. No matter our home culture, we all seem to understand the intensity, physicality, and courage that warriors, both men and women, have brought to the hunt and the battle through history. Themes of pain, sacrifice, and honor are familiar to all of us.

Today's warrior activist brings familiar qualities of courage and resolve to the battle, but instead of hunting animals or raiding neighboring villages, he fights for civil rights, environmental sanity, and dignity in politics. He does the difficult, risky work of social and cultural transformation: speaking in public, working with ideas, organizing, and persuading. Like the primal warrior, today's warrior activist is willing to endure hardship and danger for the sake of the tribe. He's willing to make personal sacrifices for the greater good.

Of course, times and challenges have changed drastically. In the Paleolithic, being a hunter–warrior was mostly a matter of killing animals and doing battle with neighboring tribes. Later, as agriculture and farming came to dominate the human experience, the warrior was assimilated into military service, where he fought alongside thousands of others in major battles.

Hunting animals and doing battle are immediate challenges, physically concentrated and unambiguous. In a Paleolithic world, the objective is supremely clear: kill an animal or defeat an enemy. But today's challenges are of an entirely different order and tone. The new warrior is now called to meet a highly ambiguous challenge, often of minimal physicality. Saving habitat and community is a complex, wicked proposition, and the challenge of modern activism is often brutally cognitive. The enemy, if there is one, is not always obvious, and success not always clear. Can the warrior stand up to this kind of challenge?

It's a big ask. The warrior spirit is ancient, restless, and seemingly ill-suited to working a laptop for months on end, sitting through endless meetings, crafting complex legal documents, or setting up nonprofit organizations. The warrior wants to engage with muscle, blood, and sinew. He wants to fight on the crux of life and death. Filling out spreadsheets or organizing fundraisers feels like a pale substitute.

But none of this matters. For the warrior, the call is to do what must be done. His personal preferences are irrelevant. His body may well crave combat and high-risk physicality, but if the tribe needs a different kind of skill, he must adapt. If the challenge requires long hours at a desk, mastering difficult technology, or navigating abstract legal and administrative concepts, this is what he must do. The warrior is someone who heeds the call, whatever form it might take.

So how do we recognize today's warrior activist? It may not be obvious. After all, we're used to thinking of warriors in striking visual terms. We think of their exceptional physicality, their rugged bodies and athletic postures. Search for "warrior" on the internet and you'll get thousands of photos of supremely buff, heavily armed men, plus a few women. But given what we know about today's challenges, we might wonder about this conventional stereotype. Outside of sports, military service, and a few occupations, few of us are called upon to perform any acts of strength or endurance for the sake of the tribe. And even in the military, an increasing percentage of the modern work is digital, not physical.

Today's warriors are often invisible. They're doing a new kind of battle, under new conditions, with new tools. They're doing the essential, often unglamorous work to protect and reshape the world. Robust physicality is always a plus, but it's not a job requirement. We're just as likely to find today's warriors slaving at their desks and clicking a mouse. They're running nonprofits, advocating for policy change, speaking and writing on behalf of people and habitat. They are teachers, doctors, nurses, cops, scientists, researchers, even writers; anyone who is working on behalf of the long body.

But don't be fooled by appearances. Today's warrior may well be tied to a computer, a phone and a desk, but the challenge remains. In days gone by, the warrior's challenge was conceptually simple: provide for the tribe, defend the tribe, hunt, and protect. Put your body on the line to keep your people alive. Fight and die if you're called to do so. But today, the warrior finds herself in a uniquely perplexing situation, especially in relationship to her home culture and the ways of her own people. She may even find herself at odds with the very people and culture that she is called to protect.

For most of history, tribal culture has been the central organizing force in human experience. Imagine a tribe of hunter-gatherers in the grip of daily survival challenges. Mother Culture holds the oral tradition, the essential, practical knowledge that keeps the tribe alive. She tells people where to hunt, how to navigate, and what kind of plants to use for cooking, medicine, and clothing. Tribes with a strong link to a coherent culture were more likely to succeed. And so our natural inclination: when times are hard, return to the familiar customs, ideas, and rituals of Mother Culture.

This is precisely what we've seen in modern America. After the trauma of 9/11, many of us reverted to the familiar and the comfortable. President George W. Bush advised us to go shopping and return to our normal lives. In the grip of chaos, fear, and uncertainty, many of us renewed our patriotism and our identification with conventional ideas and principles. When the going gets tough, we go back to Mother Culture. And when the going gets really tough, we fight back against every threat to her supremacy.

This reflex worked well enough for tens of thousands of years. We can be sure that many tribes and communities survived precisely because of this tendency to attach and return to Mother Culture. But what happens when a culture itself threatens the survival of the people? What happens when the values that are embedded in Mother Culture are actually driving the destruction of habitat and divisions among people? Suddenly, we're faced with a deep and troubling paradox: In today's world, Mother Culture is both a provider and a threat to our future. She gives us much of what we need, but her ideas, values, and institutions also facilitate the destruction of our world. It seems that even Mom gets it wrong sometimes.

And yet, despite all the evidence of looming crisis, a great many of us persist in adhering to the familiar. The darker things look, the more we double down on Mother Culture. Yes, ecosystems are collapsing all around us, but surely Mother Culture will fix everything, as she always has. Even in the face of imminent biological catastrophe, a substantial number of us insist on retreating to familiar havens of the shopping mall, the sporting venue, the TV, and the digital device. Mom will surely save us in the end.

Our inclination to embrace and defend Mother Culture in times of stress is completely understandable, but it is no longer appropriate. Mother Culture may well give us a sense of reassurance, but it's also responsible for killing entire ecosystems and threatening our future. Mother Culture—especially our modern Western version—is largely built on the domination of nature, exploitation of habitat and people, and isolation from the very source of life. And so we must question her. We must question her values and assumptions. Most of all, we must question our reflexive attachment to her ideas, traditions, and rituals. This act is supremely stressful and contrary to some of our most embedded reflexes, but it's an absolute necessity for a sane and sustainable future.

Through most of human history, the warrior was an activist for the status quo. He worked to defend the tribe, Mother Culture, and life-as-usual. He didn't blow the whistle or rock the boat. On the contrary, he reinforced the dominant narrative and stayed close to the cultural script. In turn, the people hailed his efforts and rewarded him with praise, power and opportunity. We love our conventional warriors precisely for their civil and cultural obedience.

In contrast, today's social and environmental warrior must be a counterculturalist. He must challenge Mother Culture directly and take action to transform her values, assumptions, and narrative. He must be willing to stand up and say in a loud, strong voice, "Our values are destroying our land and our future. If we follow Mother Culture blindly, our problems will become worse. We must choose a different path."

This questioning of Mother Culture is an extremely serious business. If the warrior succeeds in her questioning and activism, history will judge her a visionary and her name will be celebrated. But the odds are long, and should she fail, the punishments will be severe. Questioning Mother Culture is hard, risky, and often exhausting work. It exposes us to the wrath of traditionalists who will do everything possible to preserve the dominant culture, no matter how unsustainable it might be. People who step up to question Mother Culture will be attacked, ostracized, or marginalized. They will be denied opportunity, incarcerated or worse.

All of this puts the warrior in a supremely risky and difficult position. For thousands of generations, his primary role has been to act for the welfare of his people. Conceptually, at least, his job has been easy. But what if Mother Culture actually sanctions the destruction of the land that supports the tribe? Now the warrior's role turns back on itself. If he wants to serve his people, he must challenge their thinking, their values, and their beliefs. In this, the new warrior must be prepared for some powerful consequences. Questioning Mother Culture is one of the most serious things a person can do.

In the popular imagination, the traditional warrior had a good life. He fought epic battles against outrageous foes and suffered hardship along the way, but he usually prevailed in the end. Even if he was killed or wounded, Mother Culture stepped up to pay her respects. The warrior is given great honor for his sacrifice. His life may be hard, but at least it has a coherent sense of meaning and purpose. There is clarity here.

But today, being a warrior for the long body is no longer a simple matter. There are substantial challenges along the way, many of them psychological, social and spiritual. Rarely will today's warrior be called to step up with sword or fist. Instead, he must do battle with entrenched attitudes, outdated policies, and a culture that isn't really sure where it's going. Even worse, his victories may not be celebrated. On the contrary, he may well be attacked by the very people that he is trying to save.

The psychological challenges are acute. To act on behalf of the long body, the warrior must open up her awareness to the totality of human and ecological processes across the planet. But this big-picture awareness can be overwhelming and profoundly intimidating. Large-scale thinking opens us up to the immense amount of suffering in the world. We see the epidemics of disease, homelessness and despair in millions of people as well as the almost unimaginable levels of suffering we've inflicted on nonhuman animals and habitat around the world. This experience challenges our sense of identity and threatens to dispel some of our most cherished illusions. It can be a very uncomfortable process.

Big-scale awareness also exposes us to vast amounts of complexity and confusion. Economic, political, and biological systems interact with one another in ferociously complex ways that are fundamentally unpredictable and beyond human ability to predict. And of course, this realization makes us feel very small and helpless, as individuals and as a species. It's extremely humbling. It's no wonder that people in humanitarian organizations often complain of "compassion fatigue."

Expanding awareness can be a stressor in its own right. It doesn't attack the body directly, but it does challenge our sense of identity and psychological control. And we're not really prepared to deal with any of it. Our Paleolithic brains have been sculpted to deal with local, acute stressors like predators, wildfires, and attacks by neighboring tribes. We have no idea how to manage the prospect of planetary crisis or the realization that millions of people are suffering in poverty, forced dislocation, or human trafficking. We have no inborn capacity to deal with the threat of global climate change and human-caused species extinction.

And so we resist. Our personal lives are hard enough as it is without taking on the mega-scale challenges of global habitat destruction, climate change, human displacement, and disease. Who needs the grief, complexity, and insecurity that comes with open eyes? Consciously or otherwise, we feel this as a threat and return to our short, small-picture lives, where we can at least find some control and comfort.

It's a subconscious strategy for self-protection. We stay with the small picture because it's an effective way to insulate ourselves from the immensity of our predicaments. Unconsciously, we put it this way: "This big-picture drama is too complex, too demanding, too intimidating for me to deal with. I think I'll just burrow down into my local situation and concentrate on my narrow specialty and my pet interests."

And for a time, in a very limited way, it works. But for the warrior activist, such a retreat can never be more than a temporary refuge. Closing down awareness may be comforting, and it might even an important part of rest and recovery, but it is no place to live. It's our job to be bigger.

Even more problematic is the fact that as an activist for the future, you're going to be asking people to go against deeply held evolutionary inclinations. Human beings are wired for survival and self-preservation. We focus on the here and now because on the grassland, there might not even be a tomorrow. The distant future is an abstraction. Asking people to sacrifice for the seventh generation, especially in Western culture, is a very big request.

The situation becomes even worse when people are under stress. When the cortisol flows for months and years on end, people default to the familiar and keep their focus on local, immediate concerns. Their short-term attention and behavior may well be dysfunctional, but it is perfectly understandable. This is human neurobiology, sculpted by millennia.

Can we really expect to take a species that's been molded and sculpted by millions of years of evolution for short-term awareness to suddenly adopt a planetary-scale view of their predicament? Can we expect them to sacrifice for the sake of an abstract, long-term future? It's a powerful challenge. Even the most persuasive statistics about the threats posed by climate change and habitat destruction don't carry much weight when compared with the basic survival priorities of reproduction, rank, safety, and immediate comfort. So maybe we should be patient. After all, we're asking people to do something that's evolutionarily abnormal.

On the other hand, the facts are real, just as real as any lions or tigers or bears. We can retreat to our ancient impulses, or we can adapt to a new reality. "Being normal" is no longer a viable strategy for survival. In a sense, abnormality is our only way forward. We need to go against the grain of several million years of evolution, extending our minds and overcoming our short interests. Attention as usual isn't going to cut it anymore.

The modern warrior's role is challenging in yet another way. In conventional circumstances, the warrior is fighting for the tribe in the here and now. He's hunting or doing battle to save lives today, this season or this year. But when we take a long body view, we're inclined to see the warrior as someone who's working for the welfare of his descendants. We might well say that the warrior activist is really working for the seventh generation. In this respect, he is working for people who haven't even been born yet.

There's plenty of indigenous precedent for this perspective and role. As you may well know, the idea of acting on behalf of the seventh generation stems from Native American tradition and the Great Law of the Iroquois:

> In all of your deliberations in the Confederate Council, in your efforts at law making, in all your official acts, self-interest shall be cast into oblivion. Cast not over your shoulder behind you the warnings of the nephews and nieces should they chide you for any error or wrong you may do, but return to the way of the Great Law which is just and right. Look and listen for the welfare of the whole people and have always in view not only the past and present but also the coming generations, even those whose faces are yet beneath the surface of the ground – the unborn of the future Nation.

Oren Lyons, Chief of the Onondaga Nation, writes: "We are looking ahead, as is one of the first mandates given us as chiefs, to make sure and to make every decision that we make relate to the welfare and well-being of the seventh generation to come... What about the seventh generation? Where are you taking them? What will they have?"

With this, our popular vision of the warrior begins to shift. Suddenly, the here-and-now battles against physical adversaries seem less relevant. The new warrior is fighting and engaging in a more subtle form of combat, and has her eyes on a different kind of victory.

put your body where your mouth is

I am not what happened to me. I am what I choose to become.

C.G. Jung

Warriors are well-known for their physicality, endurance, courage, resilience, and honor, but what really distinguishes them is their willingness to accept full responsibility for their actions and even the world at large. Being a warrior means stepping up with our whole body and spirit and engaging with the world as it is.

To understand how this works, we turn to the drama triangle, a model of human relationship and orientation first described by psychologist Stephen Karpman in 1968. Often used as a tool in psychology and psychotherapy, it has powerful applications across the entire range of human experience, including warrior activism.

There are three basic roles on the triangle: victim, persecutor, and rescuer. The trouble often begins when a person identifies himself as a victim, a powerless agent in the face of external circumstance. According to the victim's narrative, the primary source of his unhappiness lies with other people, agents, and forces. He places the blame for his predicament on a persecutor, someone who's making his life miserable. At the same time, he's quick to go in search of a rescuer, someone or something that will extract him from his predicament and save the day. Naturally, these roles are fluid and subject to change; victims may become persecutors or rescuers and so on in wicked spirals of confusion, blame, recrimination, and suffering. This is why this set of relationships is often referred to as "the dreaded drama triangle."

Of course, it's essential to remember there *are* authentic victims in this world, people who deserve our attention and compassion. Just as obviously, there are authentic persecutors who deserve justice. But here we're talking about attitudes, identities, and orientations. What roles are we claiming in the world? Who is creating our lives? What kind of power do we have? These are questions of perception, agency, and responsibility. By reflecting on our roles in the triangle, we can gain a sense of clarity about what we're doing.

The process begins when we take our first steps into adulthood. Things may go well for a time, but sooner or later, we stumble and fall. We get hurt or we fail to get what we desire. Looking for a way out of our unhappiness, many of us simply react to circumstance and claim victimhood. We point a finger of blame: "The *fill in the blank* is wreaking havoc with my life. It's my parents, my genes, my childhood, my job, my boss, my spouse. It's modern culture. It's government policy. It's stress and overwork. It's the opposition party. It's everything. Everything except for me."

These accusations may well contain some elements of truth, but in a sense, this is completely beside the point. The real issue is our orientation. By claiming the role of victim, we shift responsibility away from ourselves and place it on other people, forces or substances. In effect, we externalize our mistakes and our experience.

At the same time, the self-declared victim looks to be rescued from his predicaments. He seeks out sympathetic individuals who will listen to his woes and maybe even work on his behalf to make things better. The rescuer is often a person, but it could just as well be a substance, a process, an organization, or even an idea. Anything that holds the promise of salvation can play the role.

Sometimes these strategies work for a time, but more often the victim orientation simply digs the hole of suffering deeper. By blaming perpetrators for our woes or running in search of rescue, we give away our personal power. Blaming and complaining put us into a descending spiral of reactivity, dysfunction, and unhappiness. Even worse, blame "otherizes" the world, creating a deeper sense of duality and stress. This leads to more blame, more broken relationships, more confusion, and more suffering.

Many of us have heard this story before, and it's easy to assume that victimhood is something reserved for the dysfunctional underbelly of society; alcoholics, drug addicts, and criminals come to mind. But victimhood is alive and well at every level of humanity, and no one is immune. After all, it's an easy, seductive trap. There's always plenty of blame to go around and excuses are handy: The economy is in recession, our parents were flawed, our neighborhood was in turmoil. Bullies abused us. The school system failed us, and the doctors were ineffective. The system didn't provide the kind of employment we deserved. Big corporations are destroying small business opportunities and even the Earth itself. That's why complaining has become a national sport, with entire media empires dedicated to round-the-clock finger-pointing. Donald Trump himself is a prime example of this buck-passing orientation. As Victim-in-Chief, he blames the media, intelligence agencies, and his predecessor for his inability to perform in office.

The drama triangle also tells us a great deal about today's epidemics of lifestyle disease. Public health experts are quick to pin the blame on the usual culprits of sedentary living, sugar, fat, and stress, but as we go deeper, we begin to see that our problem is actually one of orientation, attitude and responsibility. That is, far too many of us hold a passive, victimized stance in relationship to our bodies and our lives. By giving away our power to perceived perpetrators and rescuers, we give up our vitality, our physicality and our ability to control our health destiny.

Of course, there are plenty of genuine medical victims in this world, people who are struck down by genetic wild cards, drunken drivers, adulterated foods, and environmental toxins. But instead of taking action on our own behalf, many of us simply go passive and blame the world for our ailments. Lifestyle victims are quick to complain about the state of their health, and to find scapegoats for everything that ails them. In the process, they externalize responsibility: "It wasn't me that lazed around for months and years on end. It wasn't me that ate that mountain of sugar. I was seduced by circumstance."

In today's world, it's always easy to find a perpetrator. "The *fill in the blank* is destroying my health and my body." It's my genes, my childhood, my metabolism. It's modern culture. It's government policy. It's my thyroid. It's my hormones. It's gluten. It's gravity. It's Western medicine. It's stress and overwork. It's everything. Everything except for me.

Victims are famous for pointing the blame at the various perpetrators in their lives, but when that doesn't work, they turn in the other direction and seek out rescuers. These are the people, organizations, substances or ideas that will solve our troubles. "The *fill in the blank* will save my health and my life." My doctor, my massage therapist, my chiropractor, my nutritionist, my personal trainer. Andrew Weil and Dr. Oz are going to save my health. Jillian Michaels is going to save my body. Suzanne Somers is going to save me from the ravages of aging. A white-coated researcher at Big Pharma is going to cook up a cocktail of stem cells that will grow me a new organ. A psychotherapist is going to save me from depression and anxiety.

Obviously, most of our health and medical providers serve legitimate purposes, and we can be grateful for their efforts. But these relationships can also become codependent and disempowering. When we pin our hopes on rescuers, we also give away our ability to take charge of our destiny. There are times in life when we have authentic, legitimate need of health and medical support, and we're right to reach out to specialists and professionals. But as a primary attitude towards life and health, rescue does not serve us.

The way out of the drama triangle, as many spiritual teachers, therapists and coaches have suggested, is the creative orientation. This is where we exercise full responsibility and accountability. In this, we become artists and activists of our own lives, and focus our attention on the changes that we'd like to bring into being. As we move beyond old habits of blaming, complaining, excuses, and wishful thinking, life begins to open up. This becomes a world of opportunity, power, and freedom.

In this practice, we actually change our identity. Instead of blaming events in the past or hoping for a rescue in the future, we ask a new set of questions: What can I do today, right this moment, to advance my creation? Where can I exercise control? Where does my power lie?

Ultimately, it's all about attitude and orientation. Yes, some predicaments are inherently challenging, but no matter the nature of the adversity, we are free to choose our interpretations of events. We are free to choose our stories. We are free to move beyond blame and rescue.

This attitude, by the way, is the defining quality of our most popular heroes, heroines, and superheroes, both real and imagined. These people are not complainers, nor are they seduced by rescue agents, substances, or ideas. They may well be fighting epic battles against powerful forces of destruction and injustice, but they keep their energy focused on their creative goals. It's hard to imagine Martin Luther King Jr., Nelson Mandela, Rosa

Parks, Mahatma Gandhi or the tireless women of Standing Rock blaming, complaining, or looking for a rescue. Circumstances may turn against them, but they adapt.

As we take on responsibility for our creativity, we begin to see that victim responses are literally a waste of time. Blaming and complaining, hostility and anger, wishing for rescue: these kinds of mental activity are bad enough in their own right, but they also displace more important qualities and experiences of life. You can't be engaged in joyful, creative work at the same time that you're blaming the world for your unhappiness. When you choose to live on the crux of life, this all becomes so much clearer; this is precisely where the power lies.

radical responsibility

As children, we spend much of our time trying to duck responsibility. We dodge and weave as long as we can, doing our best to avoid any kind of drudgery, labor, or unpleasantness. Some of us will plateau at this point, but others will come to see that the ideal course actually lies in taking on more responsibility. As we mature, we begin to realize that responsibility, far from being a burden to be avoided, is actually the path to fulfillment. It is precisely by taking on greater levels of responsibility that we find our sense of meaning and purpose.

Radical responsibility is what distinguishes the warrior from others. The warrior doesn't just take responsibility for his own life and behaviors; he takes responsibility for *everything* around him. He takes responsibility for the state of the entire world. He takes responsibility for climate change, habitat destruction, and overpopulation. He accepts responsibility for the Deep Water Horizon, the Exxon Valdez, clear-cutting, strip mining, and factory farming. He takes responsibility for social injustice, racism, sexism, and every other form of injury that people inflict on one another. He embraces responsibility for obesity, diabetes, heart disease, and depression. He owns it all.

Obviously, the warrior didn't cause these things directly, and just as obviously, she will never be able to fix most of these problems by her own hand. But this is very much beside the point. The warrior isn't concerned about the specific causal chain of events that led to some particular problem. And she's not inclined to spend her time working out the details of who's to blame for every human calamity. Instead, she concentrates on what's here right now. She understands that the only really meaningful way to live is to accept all of it as her own. In this acceptance, she finds powerful meaning and energy.

Our willingness to accept radical responsibility is contagious. Humans are nonstop people watchers. In particular, we're highly alert for the ways in which people accept or reject responsibility for their behavior and the world at large. When people start giving away their power through blaming and complaining, others are quick to follow their lead. Before long, everyone is pointing fingers, ducking responsibility, and blaming the world for their misfortunes.

Likewise, the creative orientation is also contagious. Every time we see someone stepping up to accept responsibility for themselves and the world, we're more likely to imitate their courage. Over time, these inclinations ripple through the cultures of entire communities, schools, organizations, and even countries. In this way, making the move from victim to creator is a matter of profound social consequence. Every time we step up as warrior activists, we move the world.

the long warrior

Being an effective warrior requires an understanding of strategy, tactics and in particular, the nature of the opponent. As Sun Tzu, the Chinese military strategist famously wrote in *The Art of War*: "Know thyself, know thy enemy. A thousand battles, a thousand victories."

This all sounds very sensible, and in the conventional world of combat, it's a prescription for success. But what happens when the enemy is us? Or to be more precise, what happens when the enemy is biological and cultural? What happens when the enemy is our own population growth or our own hyper-consumptive behavior? What happens when the enemy is a narrative that sanctions the destruction of habitat and the exploitation of people? Where exactly is the locus of opposition?

We're quick to develop battle plans and prescriptions, but as so often happens, we're fighting the last war. Or, even worse, we're fighting wars in a world where the very concept of war may well be outdated. For most of us, our political activism continues to be built on the language of combat, battle, conflict, victory, and defeat. We're constantly looking for an adversary to push back against. But is this oppositional perspective still relevant or appropriate? What if duality itself is the enemy? Are we just making the problem worse?

Combative language and metaphor is so common in our culture that we can scarcely think in any other terms. Reflexively, we organize ourselves around competitions, squaring off against anyone we can find. We're addicted to combat, a theme that plays out in everything from action–adventure movies and video games to mixed martial arts. It seems that we're going blind to other forms of human relationship.

Conflict, of course, is inevitable. By its very nature, activism puts us in the path of other people and established interests. As soon as we start blowing the whistle and pushing back against shortsighted behavior, we're going to encounter resistance. Entrenched institutions, individuals, and habits don't yield easily. Safe activism is an oxymoron. When we take a stand, we make ourselves vulnerable. And sometimes, we've got to play hardball. Asking politely doesn't really move systems that are dedicated to perpetuating themselves. In the words of Frederick Douglass, "Power concedes nothing without a demand." Or as journalist Chris Hedges put it, "Only when power becomes worried about its survival does it react. Appealing to its better nature is useless. It doesn't have one." If you're not meeting opposition, that usually means you're just perpetuating the status quo.

Not only is conflict inevitable, it might also be essential. As Sebastian Junger and Chris Hedges have argued, humans may in fact be wired for war. There's something integrating and clarifying about the act of going into battle, pitting our physical, mental, and spiritual capabilities against some adversary. We say

157

that we long for peace, but deep down, our bodies really want something to push against. And if there's meaning in that fight, so much the better.

In fact, combative engagement can be powerfully therapeutic for our mental and physical health. As we've seen, the body is a collection of component parts, each with its own evolutionary history. Each one of us is a "kludge." If left unchallenged by inactivity or driven apart by incoherent stimuli and stress, the subsystems of the body drift apart in function. This makes us weaker and more vulnerable to disease. In contrast, a coherent challenge forces the subsystems of the body to work together. Fighting, in other words, can be integrating.

This is why sports, athletics, and meaningful battles can be powerfully health-promoting. Competition has its ugly side, to be sure, but there can be no denying its pull and its organizing effect on human performance and the human body. The problem, of course, is that too many of our battles are destructive or bankrupt of larger meanings. And it would be insane to go to war or concoct battles with one another as a sort of "personal growth" project. In other words, we have to be selective. There has to be coherence and meaning to our adversities.

The good news is that there is plenty of meaningful combat to be found in fighting for the long body. And we don't have to destroy anything, except perhaps anti-planet and anti-social policies and values. The fight may be less physical than we'd like, but it can still give us an integrating challenge. The battle for the long body is one of the most meaningful things we can imagine, and one worth fighting for.

martial+art

By itself, a combative orientation is incomplete. Fighting is necessary, but not sufficient. Even if we manage to achieve victory, all we've done is win a battle. And if the battle is ferocious, it may well do damage to the habitat and relationships that sustain both the victors and the vanquished. And after victory, then what? Sun Tzu and Machiavelli tell us how to win, but they don't tell us what to do next.

Our vision is often incomplete and myopic. One notable example is Deep Green Resistance, a grassroots environmental group in the Pacific Northwest. The group's organizers are pushing back hard against habitat destruction and have issued a passionate call for "taking down civilization" with heavily armed "ecological commandos." The language is combative in the extreme: "Civilization is a war against the living world." Activists are encouraged to conduct "decisive ecological warfare" and achieve victory in the "war in the woods." Their stated goal is to "cut off the roots of civilization" and "destroy power structures with militant tactics." Leaders call for a strategy of "systems disruption... aimed at identifying key points and bottlenecks in the adversary's systems (electrical, transport, financial, and so on) and engaging them to collapse those systems or reduce their functionality."

This kind of macho environmentalism might make us feel good for awhile, but it makes no sense on a practical level. In the first place, innocent people might well be harmed or even killed, and activists would likely be incarcerated. Even more to the point, such direct action would be wildly counterproductive.

It doesn't take much imagination to see what would happen if even small pieces of modern infrastructure were compromised. After all, people are *already* on edge. If modern systems started to collapse, people would instantly become desperate. And in their desperation, saving habitat is the last thing anyone would be inclined to do. As it stands, a substantial segment of the American population is armed and arguably paranoid. Gasoline or food shortages would spark violence, to both people and the natural world.

In fact, some level of social stability is absolutely essential for conservation biology to succeed. "Tearing down the structures of civilization" may sound good around a campfire, but such efforts would have hugely disruptive side effects. And when people get desperate, they'll do whatever it takes to keep their heads above water, including destroying their own future.

This is why our vision must extend beyond victory. Not only must we prepare to win, we also need to build something better. We need the martial, but we also need the art. When the warrior sees a bad idea, he must fight it, but he must also create a better idea to take its place. He must have an answer to the question, "What happens after victory?" If there is no answer, the rigors of combat may well be wasted.

For every battle, there must be a creation. For every bad idea, a better idea. For every no, a yes. For every rejection, an innovation. In fact, we might well write our own *Art of War* principle: "The supreme art of war is to subdue the enemy without fighting, and enlist him in the creation of a superior new form."

the enemy is never wrong

Fighting is all well and good, but it's easy to get wrapped up in brute force and oppositional mindsets. We take issue with a person or organization and get lost in our outrage. The enemy is guilty of a thousand transgressions, and we take each one seriously. Their behavior is not only wrong; it's unjust and unacceptable. This may all well be true, but the deeper we go into oppositional outrage, the more our minds and spirits become captive to the situation. In this sense, we've already lost.

When we get absorbed in critique and blame, we loose our ability to move and adapt. If we're going to succeed, it's essential that we keep our fluidity and our equanimity. Here we find a valuable teaching in the martial art world, where teachers often remind their students that "The enemy is never wrong." If this sounds like a preposterous statement, think again. What these teachers are saying is that we've got to stay flexible. Of course the enemy is ignorant, rude, devious, and violent. Of course he lies and cheats. But there's no point getting upset about any of it. The enemy, with all his nefarious characteristics and qualities, just *is.* Instead of complaining or wasting precious energy hoping for a better, more sensible enemy, the martial artist just gets to work with what he's got. There's nothing to be gained by wishing that our enemy has some other set of qualities. His behavior is the raw material for our art.

This fluid orientation is precisely what we need in the modern world. Many of our political adversaries are infuriating in their ignorance and their refusal to see the bigger pictures of interdependence. It's easy to get paralyzed as we bear witness to entrenched, Earth-hostile attitudes. It's tempting to wish for a better class of enemy, but we also need to work with what we've got. Life and activism would be so much easier if our opponents were reasonable, well-educated, kind, sensible and rational, but that's not our world.

So repeat after me: Donald Trump is never wrong; he just is. Sure, he's an incompetent, adolescent narcissist who poses a grave danger to democracy and the biosphere. The executive orders and cabinet appointments of early 2017 were truly outrageous and deserving of our contempt. But mere outrage simply won't get us very far. The artistry lies in seeing the danger clearly and crafting new, appropriate responses without getting bogged down in recrimination and wishful thinking. Of course Trump is a disaster for our environment and our democracy. Let's see him for what he is and get back to work.

Likewise for the chaos of our personal lives. It's tempting to long for utopian revisions to our careers, our homes, and our personal relationships. But we might do better to think of them as art projects. In other words: the is situation is never wrong. The people in our lives are never wrong. The state of our bodies is never wrong. Our emotions are never wrong. The weather is never wrong. Our careers are never wrong. And even, most mind-blowing of all, the state of the planet isn't wrong. It's all just raw material for our creative work.

Begin by examining your first impulse. For many of us, our first inclination is to judge the rightness or wrongness of whatever's in front of us. We lead with our preferences and expectations.

And before long, we're on the slippery slope of blaming, complaining, and wishing things were different.

The artist sees fault too, but she gets over her judgments quickly. She doesn't get bogged down assigning responsibility. Her job is to exercise creative vigilance, always scanning her world for opportunities for play, humor, beauty, and art, even in the midst of "impossible" situations. Of course conditions are suboptimal. Of course the block of marble is the wrong shape. Of course the bureaucracy is frustrating, markets capricious, co-workers difficult, customers demanding. The creator sees these things and may even struggle against them, but her priority is the creation. She gets over it and gets to work.

as outside, so inside

When we think of activism, most of us think of warriors who take the fight to entrenched systems, institutions, values, and culture. We think of people filing lawsuits, protesting in the streets, calling their legislators, going to meetings, hanging banners, and building support on social media. This is classic action. It's intentional and strategic, designed to overcome some undesirable state of affairs.

But this external art, valuable as it is, is only half the game. To complete the circle, we also need to take action within our own lives. We need reflection, introspection, personal growth. This is the "Be the change you wish to see in the world" kind of action. If you're appalled by the conflict and destruction you see in the world, live different. If you're annoyed by the ignorance you see around you, live different. If you're distressed by the anger and hostility you see around you, live different. This is the internal yin to the external yang of action.

In this regard, everyone has their own inclinations. Some of us like to take the world head on, while others prefer to turn inward. Some of us like to chain ourselves to pipelines, while others prefer to work on their own lives with a coach or a therapist. Taken individually, each has value, but taken together, they make each other stronger.

Naturally, extremes are always a problem. Externalists spend most of their time working on direct, "change the world" strategies and tactics. This is exciting action, and there's plenty of conflict, risk, and drama. Having an opponent to push back against makes us feel engaged and valuable. And our occasional victories can make a real, tangible difference. We love the feeling that comes with engagement.

But as an exclusive strategy, external activism can become a distortion, even an absurdity. We get so wrapped up in changing the world that we neglect to transform ourselves. This is where we find underdeveloped people fighting epic battles, but failing to heed the very message that's embedded in their cause. Nothing is so sad as the external warrior who can't bring the metaphors of his work down into his own personal life. Even when victories are achieved, they ring hollow.

Likewise, the extremes of internal activism can be equally absurd. This is where the internalist turns his personal development into a full-time avocation: an endless series of retreats, self-help books, meditation, counselors, coaches, and therapists.

He focuses exclusively on his body, his spirit, and his personal life transformation. It's good work, to be sure, but it can also be an escape and an excuse to avoid the bigger realities of the day.

Internal activism is essential, but the fact remains that there are external battles that must be fought. There are policies, organizations, and ideas that must be opposed. It may well be true that personal enlightenment can have a subtle, quantum-field effect on the whole of humanity, but in many cases, lawsuits, phone calls, and protests just work better. Changing the trajectory of planet-hostile and people-hostile organizations requires more than personal reflection and transformation. It also requires gritty, messy engagement. It requires speaking, writing, going to meetings, and standing your ground. Sometimes we have to let go of our personal issues and get to work on the issue in question. Even Gandhi marched to the sea.

Ultimately, there must be a *bothness* to our efforts, a yin and yang of activism. The good news is that each can support the other. Introspection can make us better external activists, just as experience in conflict teaches us powerful lessons about ourselves. This means there are at least two reasons to visit your member of Congress, march in the street, and organize your neighbors. First, you might change some minds and help move the needle on important policies. Second, you'll learn more about yourself.

When we get the balance right, internal and external action combine to form a virtuous circle of experience and learning. Personal insights and reflection inform the way we work in the world. Likewise, our experiences in taking action teach us about our assumptions, our inclinations, and our disposition.

This orientation sheds new light on our lives. In conventional conversation, we're accustomed to thinking of our "practices" in a rather narrow way. We've got our yoga practices and our meditation practices, but these are almost exclusively personal. But now, in light of our new realities, activism can and should be considered a practice in its own right.

beautiful trouble

It's easy to assume that the warrior activist is a grim soldier for the cause. He's a strong, no-nonsense kind of person. Courageous, but simple. Solid and dedicated. All true, but there's another side to our hero. This is where the warrior merges with another popular archetype, the trickster. Common across many human cultures, the trickster keeps things slightly off balance, questions the status quo, and in the process, keeps us from being too consumed with our own sense of importance. The trickster has great intelligence and secret knowledge, and he uses it to disrupt normal rules and conventional behavior. He bends the rules and questions authority. He's a cultural monkey wrench.

This is where the warrior–trickster serves as a natural counter-weight to Mother Culture, pointing out her foolishness and her limitations. In fact, the presence of the trickster archetype shows great wisdom. Cultures that honor the trickster are less likely to become dogmatic, domineering, or aggressive. By including an internal prankster, they avoid the trap of taking themselves too seriously. It's a move toward modesty and humility.

Of course, tricks and pranks can be great fun. Violating cultural norms and expectations is exciting and makes for good theater, but it won't do to simply go out and mess things up at random. It's essential that we consider both our ends and our means. In our passion, it's tempting to advocate for extreme actions against our opponents. After all, we've got plenty of reason. Our position is strong. We're on the side of everything that's good and right and just. The forces of destruction must be stopped, the biosphere must be saved, social injustice must be rectified. The end is clear, and we must fight to make it so.

But no matter our passion, the means are essential and must be respected. Beautiful means are just as important as any outcome. All the great activists have seen this clearly:

Ralph Waldo Emerson: "Cause and effect, means and ends, seed and fruit cannot be severed; for the effect already blooms in the cause, the end preexists in the means, the fruit in the seed."

Aldous Huxley: "…the means employed determine the nature of the end produced."

Mahatma Gandhi: "Ends and means are inseparable. "Realization of the goal is in exact proportion to that of the means… As the means, so the end."

In the aftermath of the 2016 election, this reminder is more important than ever. Our anger is hot, and people are furious. It's tempting to counter falsehoods and indignities with equal and opposite statements of incivility. It's easy to sling mud and get down in the gutter. It's tempting to get violent with our words or our behavior. But, as New York Times columnist Frank Bruni pointed out in January 2017, this is a path to long-term defeat.

By getting wrapped up in our emotional outrage, we simply prolong our agony. As Bruni wrote, the solution is "To rant less and organize more. To resist taunts and stick with facts. To answer invective with intelligence." It may be fun to get down in the mud, but there's too much at stake to waste time on name-calling.

A particularly striking example of beautiful trouble took place in a rural village in India in 1974. A local contractor declared his intention to cut a local forest, but village people opposed the cut and began to mobilize. They considered their options and planned their action. When the big day came, the women of the village cooked a great feast for everyone in the village, including the men with chainsaws. Then, just as everyone was enjoying the afterglow of good food and company, the women took to the forest, wrapping their arms around the trees in protest. The well-fed contractors soon gave up their effort. Who would dare attack the people who had just fed them?

Another striking example took place in October 2016, near Anacortes, Washington. Climate activists resolved to turn a valve to shut off the flow of tar sands oil to the refinery. But instead of doing sabotage under the cover of night, they brought a film crew and did the deed in broad daylight, with perfect intention and transparency. The whole point was to be seen; they posted the entire event on their website. They even left flowers at the site, which were later entered into evidence in court. During the trial, the arresting officer admitted that this was the first time someone had left flowers at the scene of the "crime."

beautiful spirit

As we open our eyes to the scope and depth of environmental and social destruction around the world, it's tempting to fall into the well of misanthropy, cynicism, and species-self-loathing. While many of us remain attached to delusions of human supremacy, another segment of our society goes in the other direction entirely. We hate the species that destroys the world that we love; "We suck" goes a common refrain. And from there, it's but a short step to blame, division, hatred, and even violence.

It's all perfectly understandable and forgivable. These are normal human reactions. When the forest, grassland, or pond of your childhood is destroyed to make room for freeways, condos, and shopping malls, it's natural and essential to react with anger, even rage. When your future is imperiled by greed, corruption, and short-sightedness, it's easy to fall into despair, hatred, and bitterness. But these emotions must eventually give way. The warrior feels these things too, more acutely than most. But he keeps to the higher ground. He lets the anger and bitterness go, then gets back to the work.

This is where our activism becomes a spiritual act. This is where we turn to loving, non-violent combat. We engage the fight, but keep our humanity. We protest the policies, the behaviors, and the values that harm our world, but we honor the dignity of the people involved. Obviously, some people and organizations commit horrible acts of violence and ignorance against the long body. But in the main, most of the agents of destruction are actually victims themselves. Many of the people who do violence to habitat by deforestation, oil extraction, and overfishing are themselves being exploited by wealthy corporate interests. These people deserve our compassion too. The real perpetrators are further up the chain.

Above all, the warrior keeps his eye on the long body. Fighting and protest are essential, but demonizing is not. People, no matter how misguided, are still people. And those people are best persuaded with love, respect, and appeals to intelligence. The warrior takes the fight to the behaviors and values that destroy our world, but she gives her adversaries their humanity, even when they attempt to take away her own.

(possibly inconsistent
with the Chris Hedges
quote on page 157

The Master Aptitude

Doubt is not a pleasant condition, but certainty is an absurd one.

Voltaire

Our modern human predicament is an epic, unprecedented challenge. We're face-to-face with an extinction crisis, habitat destruction on a vast scale, and an escalating humanitarian catastrophe. And to top it off, we're caught in the midst of a species-wide identity crisis. Some people want to go back to a Paleolithic golden age, while others want to go forward to some kind of technological wonderland. And in the midst of all of it, Mother Culture isn't really providing much in the way of guidance. We're experiencing epic levels of cognitive dissonance as we try to square our self-image with the undeniable fact that we're well on our way to making the biosphere uninhabitable. Welcome to the planet of ambiguity.

The problems themselves are bad enough, but it's the doubt and dissonance that really eats away at us. We'll do almost anything to make the feeling go away. As individuals, we have all sorts of "strategies" to manage the uncertainty, most of them unconscious. When ambiguity creeps into our lives, we drop out of engagement and go in search of amusement. We shop. We ingest all manner of mind- and body-altering substances. We exercise like demons to make our bodies "bulletproof." We work around the clock. We flee to the past or the future. We turn to extremism and dogma or hitch our lives to gurus, experts, and authority figures. Above all, we start looking for adversaries: people, institutions, and ideas we can blame for our discontent.

As a culture, we do the same kinds of things, only worse. In fact, we might well describe modern Western culture as a concentrated effort to make human life ambiguity-proof. Our dwellings, cities, weapons, tools, energy systems, and sophisticated knowledge are all deployed strategically to keep uncertainty at bay. Almost never do we stop to question the wisdom of new innovations. If there's even a sliver of possibility that a new device, machine, or product will reduce our ambiguity or uncertainty in some small way, we'll happily go along for the ride.

The consumer market is a notorious enabler of this process. Marketers work overtime to ease the minds of potential customers, dispensing analgesic remedies in a thousand forms. Young entrepreneurs are told to "find a pain point and solve it." Or, if that fails, create a new pain point from scratch. If a consumer is experiencing any kind of frustration in life, however minor, start a company and offer a solution. And, as frustrated consumers looking to make our doubt and dissonance go away, we're more than happy to click the "buy now" button. We feel better for a short while, but the fundamental problem remains.

life is ambiguity

But the uncertainty isn't going to go away. It's the ocean that we swim in. It's in the air we breathe. And it's with us every moment of our lives. After all, who could imagine a more ambiguous situation than the one we currently inhabit? An occasionally sentient species on a pale blue dot, orbiting an unremarkable star at the edge of a galaxy somewhere in the vast reaches of space? Life takes us by surprise, and after that, there are no guarantees. We're just one breath away from eternity. Experts like to tell us how the world works, but no one really knows how we got here or why.

In fact, today's bio-human predicament is easily the greatest koan ever told. Not even a thousand-year-old Zen master could come up with a riddle so confounding and perplexing: A semi-conscious species, suddenly becoming aware that it is destroying the habitability of its only home in the known universe. And that's just the entry-level version. We're also face-to-face with the realization that the ultimate fate of any species is to go extinct, and that in all likelihood, we are no different. In this sense, it makes no difference what we do. Our intelligence, our consciousness, and our sense of significance may well vanish like a dream.

Some say that the purpose of a Zen koan is to crash the rational system. By putting the mind into a state of maximum confusion, we bring the gears of conscious deliberation to a halt and put ourselves in position for full engagement with life. Perhaps so, but for those who care to ponder the full depth and breadth of the human predicament, the ambiguity seems as vast as the reaches of intergalactic space.

No one understood the nature of our predicament better than the Buddha. The first of his Four Noble Truths holds that "All life is suffering," or a better translation, "All life is impermanent." Human life is fundamentally unsatisfactory, which is to say, it fails to provide the certainty and assurance that we so often desire. It offers a myriad of experiences, some beautiful and some hostile, but all are temporary. Our loved ones, our bodies, and now, even our biosphere, it seems, are in various states of decay. There is nothing we can do that will change this fundamental fact.

Our mistake is to believe that ambiguity is a solvable problem, that it can and should be fixed. Just get the right education, the good job, a great partner, and all will be well. Exercise really hard and eat all the right foods and you'll never succumb to disease. Hang out with all the right people and they'll support your every need. But it's all delusion. No amount of education, technology, wealth, exercise, or social status will insulate us from the uncertainty that's woven into life.

Our inability to tolerate ambiguity is more than just a philosophical failing. It often has disastrous systemic consequences. Most obviously, it's hard on our health. When we're unable to deal with the uncertainties of life, we're more likely to turn to sugar, alcohol, drugs, and all the rest. But it gets worse. Our inability to tolerate ambiguity also wrecks human relationships and careers. We become impatient with differences, demand assurances, run from complexity, and reject those who disagree with us.

Even worse, our inability to tolerate ambiguity also plays out at the large-scale level of environmental destruction. The present age of global uncertainty feels extremely tenuous, but instead of living with it, we turn up our anxious activity and redouble our efforts to get what we can before it's too late. We increase our rate of consumption and start hoarding wealth. And it's contagious. Before long, everyone gets into the act, racing to extract whatever they can before the whole thing falls apart. Even the election of 2016 can be seen in these terms. Unable to deal with the ambiguity of our modern predicament, many of us turned toward an autocratic personality who promised quick and easy solutions for complex, systemic problems.

wicked problems

Ambiguity is bad enough, but wickedness may be even worse. As we've seen, our encounter with the modern world is not a single, linear puzzle. It's multidimensional. It's ecological–spiritual–political–economic–cultural. It's multilayered, massively interconnected, extremely dynamic, and unprecedented. In other words, it's "wicked."

This may sound like pop culture slang, but there's actually a sophisticated definition here. The term "wicked problem" is widely recognized among systems theorists, urban planners, and those who grapple with large-scale social and design challenges. In this sense, the word *wicked* doesn't mean bad or evil, but something so complex that it dwarfs our capacity for understanding. The generally accepted definition goes like this:

Every wicked problem is novel or unique.

There is a no stopping rule; you can't hit the pause button.

Wicked problems have no single cause, no single effect, and no given alternative solution.

Sincere and well-informed experts disagree about the fundamental nature of the problem.

There is no single "best practice." Experience, in other words, isn't much help.

Wicked problems are bigger and more challenging than conventional, complex problems. A Rubik's cube is a hard problem, but it's not wicked. Building a bridge is complex and difficult, but it's not wicked. According to Jay Rosen, professor of journalism at New York University, wicked problems have these features:

It's hard to say what the problem is, to define it clearly, or to tell where it starts and stops. There is no 'right' way to view the problem, no definitive formulation. The way it's framed will change what the solution appears to be. Someone can always say that the problem is just a symptom of another problem, and that someone will not be wrong. There are many stakeholders, all with their own frames, which they tend to see as exclusively correct. Ask what the problem is and you will get a different answer from each. The problem is interconnected to a lot of other problems; pulling them apart is almost impossible… It gets worse. Every wicked problem is unique, so in a sense there is no prior art, and solving one won't help you with the others.

All of our big public policy problems are wicked: education, environment, poverty, housing, economic development, health care, criminal justice, political reform. Almost everyone agrees that these systems aren't working as well as they should, but we can hardly agree on how to frame the problems or where to start. This is why politics is such a messy business. Modern life seems to consist of nothing so much as wicked problems stacked on top of one another in one big cluster of mega-wickedness.

And that's just the beginning. Mismatch itself is a monstrously wicked problem, completely without precedent. Our primal, ancient bodies are struggling mightily to find their way in an alien world. The modern world keeps changing at a furious pace, but the human mind–body remains substantially the same as it ever was. Thus, the gap between our bodies and modern reality continues to widen with each passing moment.

Wickedness is not just something that we find at large scales of public policy, society, or the human predicament. Even our personal lives feel wicked. Our relationships, our families, and our careers often feel like clusters of chaos and confusion. On many days, we don't have the slightest idea how to frame our lives or where to begin. We structure a task or relationship in one way, only to have our partners, bosses, or children frame it as something altogether different. More and more, it seems like the universal answer to every query about our lives is, "It's complicated."

It's tempting to suppose that wickedness is some kind of special case, a perfect storm of complexity that comes into our lives on rare occasions. But maybe we'd do better to view wickedness as an integral part of the human condition, woven into the very fabric of our lives. As we've seen, a situation is wicked when it's massively interlinked, dynamic, and open-ended. What better description could there be of our personal encounters with life itself? Life takes us by surprise, and now we're here, standing in the middle of the most astonishing conundrum imaginable. In this respect, the art of living is really the art of navigating our encounters with ambiguity, uncertainty, and wickedness.

willpower arts

The secret of all existence is simply to learn to wait.

Robert Heinlein
Stranger in a Strange Land

The warrior's ability to tolerate ambiguity is a matter of temperament and character, but it's also a matter of willpower. This is an essential skill for anyone who's trying to live an effective, happy life, especially in our modern, alien environment.

Today we are overwhelmed by temptation. Not just by the classic seductions of greed, lust, sloth, and envy that have always lured humans into regrettable behavior, but by an entirely new class of attractions: flashing lights, special offers, new products, outrageous claims, fake news, and instant everything. In every minute of every day, powerful, well-funded industries throw gasoline on the fire of our passions, beguiling us with ever more hyperbolic promises, all designed to appeal to our most primitive instincts. The internet has turned the modern marketplace into one vast convenience store, a planet-sized vending machine for the satisfaction of every human desire. In early 2017, a promotional program for Amazon Prime lured customers with the claim "No patience required."

In this high-temptation environment, we are at risk for all sorts of calamities and afflictions: substance abuse, broken relationships, bankruptcy, incarceration, and lifestyle disease. These are plenty bad enough, but even more catastrophic is the loss of personal power that comes with willpower failure. Unable to resist temptation or delay gratification, we become vulnerable to every passing stimulus. Unable to wait, we can only react. Worst of all, we lose our ability to create. We become ineffective activists for our health and the long body.

The good news is that we understand a lot more about willpower than ever before. Thanks in large measure to social psychologist Walter Mischel and his legendary "marshmallow test," we now know the fundamentals of self-control. Even better, we know how to train for it. As you probably remember, Mischel gave a set of four-year-old children a simple choice: "You can

179

have one marshmallow now, but if you wait, you can have two." Being a good scientist, he recorded each student's performance and tracked them over the years. The results clearly demonstrated the power of self-control, not just in the routine choices of day-to-day living, but in the overall trajectory of life. Children who were able to delay gratification were more likely to succeed in academics, career, health, and personal life. Clearly, willpower is vital to how we live and who we might become.

Of course, self-control has long been an essential element of human success. As our Paleolithic ancestors developed larger brains and more complex social lives, we also gained proficiency in hunting. But hunting calls for some serious self-control; you can't simply go charging off into the bush, chasing after game on impulse, and expect to succeed. You may need to sit still for hours, stalk with great care, or coordinate complex maneuvers with your hunting party. If you can't regulate your impulses, you may well go hungry.

Later, as we entered the age of agriculture, discipline and willpower became even more important to our success. Human time horizons grew longer. We planted crops, expecting to be gratified months later. We built immense monuments that took decades or even generations to complete. The construction of cities, roads, energy systems, and modern technology have all relied on our ability to wait.

Today, our need for self-control has become even more pronounced. As the modern world becomes ever more complex, we are called upon to exercise almost heroic levels of self-control in everyday life. An avalanche of innovation has given us incredible new ideas, tools, and media, as well as instant food and drink temptations in almost every direction. This adds up to an unprecedented level of distraction and impulse challenge. To make matters even more difficult, we now must sustain our career aspirations for decades, from kindergarten all the way through graduate school and beyond. For modern humans, the marshmallow is many years away.

willpower is a muscle

For centuries, teachers, scholars and religious leaders have taught that willpower is simply a matter of character. People with a strong moral foundation have the ability to resist temptation, but others fall short. If people are unable to resist temptation, it's their own fault. Good people resist the lure of the marshmallow, but bad people fall for it.

Today, our more sophisticated view holds that willpower is largely a function of our brains and bodies. Character still has a role to play, but in general, our ability to inhibit impulse comes down to the interplay between neural circuits, brain structure, hormones, and neurotransmitters; it's how we use our brains that makes the difference.

Most importantly, we now know that self-control is a neuro-physical capability that's trainable, just like a muscle. This metaphor has been invoked by many, most notably by Roy Baumeister and John Tierney in *Willpower: Rediscovering the Greatest Human Strength* and Kelly McGonigal in *The Willpower Instinct*. Numerous studies demonstrate that active, disciplined training increases our ability to exercise control over behavior. The effect is both specific and general; we can train ourselves to inhibit particular urges and impulses in context, but it's also the case that any kind of training in delayed gratification will strengthen our will.

In a way, the moralists were half-right. People become more self-controlled by practicing self-control; disciplined educational environments tend to promote more disciplined behavior. This is why sports, arts, music, and academic training are important parts of a whole-life education. Children who learn these disciplines may not use the specific arts in adult life, but the inhibitory powers that they learn are often transferable to other domains. A child who learns how to delay gratification in school, music class, martial art, or sports is better positioned to meet the discipline challenges of later life.

two systems

Our willpower challenge is a natural consequence of lopsided, unbalanced forces within our bodies. It's a tenuous relationship: On one hand, the deep body is ancient, fast, powerful and unconscious. Its primary interest is survival. It is constantly vigilant to threats, and can take control of the entire mind–body system if necessary. On the other hand is our conscious brain, orchestrated by the prefrontal cortex. This system is new and incredibly sophisticated, but it's also fragile and notoriously unreliable.

When all goes well, the prefrontal brain inhibits impulses coming from the deep body; it keeps the brakes on. But when stress hits the fan, things can go out of balance in a hurry. The ancient, primal parts of the deep brain begin to assert control. We experience a "reptilian takeover" of our minds and behavior. Even worse, stress hormones begin to erode the function of the prefrontal cortex itself, further limiting our ability to regulate our impulses. In other words, the balance of power begins to shift from new to old. In effect, we travel backward in evolution to a more reactive primal state.

Sometimes our willpower muscle is well-rested and strong, but other times it becomes fatigued and loses its ability to inhibit impulses. This "depletion hypothesis" tells us that willpower is a limited resource, but it also presents us with a paradox. As Kelly McGonigal put it, "because every act of willpower depletes willpower, using self-control can lead to losing control." This is why willpower lapses are more common late in the day. We might well be paragons of virtue in the morning, but then, after ten hours of inhibition and self-regulation, we head for the bar and make fools of ourselves.

Unfortunately, many of us fail to appreciate just how much demand we place on prefrontal willpower in the course of our daily lives. Most of us believe that our primary willpower challenge lies in reining in our excess consumption of food, intoxicants, sloth, and lust. If we had just a little more willpower, the thinking goes, we'd lose some weight, get back in shape, and feel like an Olympic athlete.

But we use also our willpower in myriad ways that go far beyond the obvious challenges of carbohydrates, alcohol, and sex. As it turns out, most of us put immense demands on our willpower in nearly every minute of the modern day. We use willpower any time we attempt to juggle the thousand competing details of work, school, and family life. We use willpower when we repeatedly call our attention back to some unpleasant task, when we're forced to rearrange our carefully crafted plans, and when we're forced to remain seated through endless meetings. We use willpower when we're called upon to read and revise difficult material, when we really want to express an opinion but are silenced by social constraints, and when we're working on a deadline, trying to force our performance into a narrow window of time.

In short, most of us in the modern world are running our willpower capability just about as hard as it can go, most of the time. No wonder we break down when the dessert cart comes around and our friends tell us it's time for another round.

general advice

Fortunately, there are several reliable strategies that can help keep our willpower intact. In *The Marshmallow Test*, Walter Mischel suggests that we boil our practice down to three key actions: dampen, delay, and distance. Dampen the raging fires of the hot system with cooling, rational thoughts, especially about the rewards that will come by way of self-control. Delay gratification, even for a few minutes, and allow the hot system to cool down. Create distance, by reframing our situation and our willpower challenge. In other words, we look to call the marshmallow by some other name. In the original test, some children imagined the marshmallow as a puffy white cloud. Others imagined it in a picture frame. Likewise, look at your willpower challenge from an airplane, from a thousand feet above the ground or a mile away. Look at it as a trivial distraction from your primary mission, as mere noise in the system, something easily disregarded.

It's also essential that we recognize and honor the so-called depletion events that drain our inhibitory powers throughout the day. A hyper-focused project at work, a tense meeting, an emotional family encounter, a travel screw-up, even a national or global crisis: all of these events deplete our willpower resources. If you don't allow for recovery, and go straight into another high-pressure challenge, you'll be setting yourself up for failure or worse.

Avoid willpower depletion by conserving your cognitive resources. Limit your exposure and consumption of digital information. Try not to drink too much from the fire hose. Make peace with the idea that you're just not going to absorb it all. Even a cognitive superstar can only read and assimilate a fraction of the material that's available. No matter how much your read or how hard you try, you're not going to absorb more than a fraction of it anyway. So resist the impulse to gather ever more data. Read less. Do less homework. Simplify your technology and use less of it.

One of the most unrecognized depletion events in the modern world might be called the "spring fever effect." Imagine this picture: the weather is glorious outside and life is returning to the world, but you've got a pile of indoor work that must be done. For those of us who are deeply wired for prehistory, this is a torturous experience, one that requires an enormous amount of prefrontal control. We look out the window and see the natural light streaming down. We see the trees waving in the breeze. We know that the earth is throbbing with life, and it's just outside the door. Our bodies crave the outdoor experience, but the weight of obligation, responsibilities, and legalities force us to stay where we are, fingers on the keyboard. Now our prefrontal brains are working overtime, pumping out as much inhibition as they can muster, trying to keep our deep primal nature subdued long enough to get the work done. This is massively expensive and exhausting. By the end of the day, the cortex is depleted and we're vulnerable to impulse. Unless we recognize this event for what it is, we're likely to suffer a willpower collapse in some other part of our lives.

Naturally, some of us will go too far and attempt to exercise maximum self-control at all times. But the depletion hypothesis suggests that this is a flawed strategy. We know that discipline can be trained, but beyond the tipping point, the self-control system becomes brittle and prone to disaster. This is why we need some slack in our willpower system. This implies a firm kind of discipline, one that holds the line, but not too tightly; one that keeps us away from the worst temptations while still allowing us some room to maneuver; one that regulates the hot, passionate parts of our brains, but still gives us room for pleasure, self-compassion, and kindness.

We see a good example of such an approach in the world of diet and eating. As most of us know, trying to maintain perfect dietary discipline often backfires in the face of daily realities; sometimes the body simply takes over and eats what it wants.

Rigid diets tend to fail catastrophically. As an alternative, re-al-world coaches often advise their clients to eat the highest possible quality for 80 percent of the time and let the other 20 percent fall where it may. It's not a perfect system, but that's pre-cisely what makes it work. By allowing some flexibility, it doesn't trigger fear or deprivation psychologies. In turn, this makes it easier to stick to the solid 80.

With this in mind, our practice lies in keeping a sense of proportion and balance in our lives. Maintain a sense of control, but allow some room for interpretation, pleasure, and wildness. Run a firm ship. Regulate your worst behavior with firewalls and real discipline, but give in to life and love. Hold the line as long as you can, but allow yourself to be seduced from time to time. Paradoxically, this will give you precisely what you're looking for: an integrated, disciplined practice with just enough flex to keep your creativity alive.

the wisdom of insecurity

The ideal art, the noblest of art: working with the complexities of life, refusing to simplify, to 'overcome' doubt.

Joyce Carol Oates

The warrior is strong. She understands her predicament and resolves to live squarely in the midst of confusion and insecu-rity without running, hiding or reaching for a distraction. This aptitude was famously described in an inverse manner by the poet John Keats in a letter of 1817:

> … at once it struck me, what quality went to form a Man of Achievement especially in literature and which Shakespeare possessed so enormously–I mean Negative Capability, that is when man is capable of being in uncertainties, Mysteries, doubts without any irritable reaching after fact and reason.

For the warrior activist, this means living right smack in the middle of exposure, without impulsively reaching for closure or safety. She knows that doubt, however unpleasant, is the status quo. It's in the air that she breathes. Her courage lies in her willingness to step up and perform, in spite of the unknown.

We like to think that the warrior is a paragon of confidence, but she is just as afflicted as any of us, perhaps more so. She feels the anxiety of doubt and knows the nagging fear that she might not be doing the right thing. But still, she refuses to dodge reality. She refuses to hide out or engage in practices that would insulate her from uncertainty. She stands squarely in the middle of all of it. And from that position, she acts.

As for the warrior, so too for the artist. In fact, we might well say that wickedness itself is the artist's raw material. When beginning a project, she has only a vague idea of what he is trying to create. He can't possibly plan it all in advance or map out every step. Things are going to change. The materials are going to transform. His body is going to shift. His hands will learn new sequences. New insights will leap to mind. If she tries to force his will onto the work, something will break.

That's why spirit is the essential ingredient in all our creations. Wickedness cannot be mastered, or even truly understood. The process is far, far bigger than the artist himself. He can bring his skills to bear, but they may not be enough. His vision may fail. His senses and skills may prove inadequate. And he knows all this before he begins.

No matter how hard we try, our efforts to make our lives ambiguity-proof always seem to fail. And in fact, they deepen the very problem they were meant to solve. Our problem isn't insecurity—it's our inability to live with insecurity. No one understood this better than Alan Watts:

"There is a contradiction in our desire to be secure in a universe whose very nature is fluidity and movement...If I want to be secure, that is, protected from the flux of life, I am wanting to be separate from life. Yet, it is this very sense of separateness that makes me feel insecure. In other words, the more security I can get, the more I shall want..."

This may be the hardest lesson for us to learn. How to just sit in the middle of it all. To just sit in the middle of ecological ambiguity, overshoot, climate change, social injustice, Donald Trump, and the sixth extinction. Grasping for security and trying to bulletproof our lives will only make things worse.

So the next time you're stuck in a financial, social, physical, or existential predicament that's ambiguous, wicked, and uncertain just remember: Your situation is normal. Keep your focus, keep creating, and above all, relax.

Truing the Wheel

The spokes of wheels are like the spokes of our lives: our family, our community, everything that supports us. The center of our existence is the hub. And notice that when the wheel spins, everything is moving except for the center. That's us, you know. Our wheels need to be true and straight. Be mindful of them, and tighten the spokes in the right way.

James Veliskakis
Three Lives: From Biker to Buddhist

Lack of systemic wisdom is always punished. If you fight the ecology of a system, you lose—especially if you 'win.'

Gregory Bateson ✦

As we've seen, life in our alien environment can be a profoundly disintegrating experience. Our minds are distracted and fragmented. Stress and time pressure pull us in multiple directions while our bodies do the best they can to keep the pace. In our frustration, we look for an antagonist, something to push against. Surely there must be people, organizations, institutions, or ideas that we can fight and maybe defeat. If we can win the battle, things will surely get better.

But this dualistic style has some serious limitations. The problems that cause us the most trouble are rarely concentrated in single points of agency, malevolence, or stupidity. More likely, they're embedded, diffuse, and spread out over landscapes, institutions, cultures, and now, even the entire planet. Our enemies are everywhere and nowhere. Our problems, in other words, are radically systemic.

We hear this revealed in thousands of expert interviews on radio, TV, and the internet. A certain pattern emerges. The interviewer wants to know about some pressing social, cultural or biomedical problem. Almost without fail, the expert explains that "it's way more complicated than we thought." He describes some of the many linkages, contingencies, and relationships that affect the problem in question, and concludes that "more study is needed." In other words, our problems with health, habitat, and social justice are not single-issue problems. We act as if there's one single solution to terrorism, climate change, health care, inequality, and education, but these things are distributed across our systems, woven into the totality of our social and cultural organism.

This becomes obvious when we try to take stock of our modern planetary predicament. Depending on your view, our troubles are driven by one or all of these factors:

- Biology and the expansion of the human population
- A culture of domination and exploitation
- Rapacious capitalism and the blind pursuit of profit
- Runaway technological development
- Shortsighted individual psychology, driven by Paleolithic impulses

All of these contribute to our predicament. The problem, of course, is that each of these challenges calls for a wildly different solution. If we take a strictly biological approach, we try to dampen human population growth and impact. If we take a regulatory approach, we try to rein in some of the worst corporate abuses. If we take a cultural approach, we try to change the stories that drive human behavior. And of course, we have to do all of these things in concert. In other words, our efforts need to be radically systemic as well. We need to weave our ideas and our solutions into the very fabric of the modern world. Specialized, one-off "solutions" will get us nowhere.

The problem is that most human and biological systems are too complex and dynamic for the human mind to fully comprehend. Organizational systems, government systems, ecosystems, personal lives: when we try to absorb every detail one at a time, our minds bog down. We sink into a quagmire of detail, and some of us never return. We'd do better to adopt a model that embodies the essential nature of a complex system while still being easy to grasp. For this, the bicycle wheel is ideal.

The beauty of the bicycle wheel lies in its interdependent structure. In order for the wheel to roll true, the rim, spokes, and hub must be in the right relationship to one another. Each element participates in supporting the entire structure. The load, in other words, is shared.

This is something every young bicycle mechanic discovers in short order. Your new bicycle rolls true, but one day you find that you've got a wobble. You can feel it in the ride, and you can hear it as the rim scrapes against the brake pad. So you flip your bike over, grab a wrench, spin the offending wheel, and go to work. Immediately the challenge becomes obvious. Any one adjustment affects the entire structure. You might get lucky and turn the spoke nipple just the right amount and in the right direction. But more likely, you'll have to fuss with multiple adjustments that ripple across the entire wheel. It's an art.

As a radically interdependent structure, the bicycle wheel reminds us of Buckminster Fuller's concept of *tensegrity*, or "tensional integrity." A tensegrity structure is a unitary system of interrelationship and mutual dependency. Fuller's creation of the geodesic dome was a prime example, but engineers and architects have used tensegrity principles to build bridges, buildings, and other structures around the world.

But tensegrity is more than an engineering concept. It's also a feature of a healthy ecosystem, where each organism and species forms a spoke in the larger whole. If one species-spoke becomes too loose or too short, it naturally affects the totality of the wheel. Every plant, every animal, every microorganism participates in the regulation and health of the entire system. Even

Aristotle was in on this idea. In an early work on biology, he wrote, "Everything is for the sake of something else."

In fact, we see these kinds of tensegrity relationships all around us, from the intricate balances inside our bodies all the way to communities, organizations, and entire ecosystems. The musculoskeletal system of the human body is a perfect example; some people call this *biotensegrity*. No one muscle is responsible for any human movement. No one structure is responsible for stabilizing any joint. It's always a shared effort. This is something that every athlete and physical therapist knows. Some muscles are dominant in particular movements, but they never act alone. Isolation is impossible. Tensegrity has also been demonstrated at the level of cells, membranes, and even the cytoskeleton.

It's also safe to say that most successful families, organizations, companies, and relationships also have a sense of tensegrity built into their structure and their culture. Shared participation in the totality is vital for success. In all these settings, the wheel reminds us that we are part of a larger ecological and social whole. Dr. Martin Luther King, Jr. might well have been talking about a wheel when he wrote, "We are caught up in an inescapable network of mutuality ... I can never be what I ought to be until you are what you ought to be, and you can never be what you ought to be until I am what I ought to be. This is the way the world is made." As he so famously put it, we are part of "a single garment of destiny." Or, as the Buddha taught: "Everything depends on everything else."

Bicycle wheels, tensegrity structures, mandalas, and unitary symbols of all kinds: These express our universal interest in integration and ecological intelligence. All of us desire to become one; with bodies, our habitats, our organizations, communities, and the cosmos. Beginning at birth, we experience a compelling drive to attach to a caregiver and form a bond. Likewise, we form strong attachments to place and the land around us. And of course, the word health derives from the root word meaning "whole."

As Carl Jung and other observers of the human condition have noted, we all have a natural, innate drive toward integration; no matter how badly we're injured, distracted, traumatized, or dislocated, our bodies and subconscious minds are always seeking a path back to wholeness. So it's no wonder that teachers, trainers, coaches, and mental health professionals all across the spectrum are united in this quest to put things together. When you get right down to it, all of us are in the integration business.

This systemic approach is a common theme in many disciplines. We hear it in the world of athletic training, where coaches stress the importance of integrated movement and tell their athletes, "Lift the weight with your whole body!" We also hear it in psychotherapy, where counselors encourage their patients to adopt integrative narratives that bring their lives together into a single, coherent whole. And we even hear it in unlikely places, where strategists in business, law, education, design, and public policy advise us to reach for an integrated "systems approach."

And of course, this circular, tensegrity view is a common feature of native cultures around the world. A classic example comes from the Native American elder Black Elk: "Everything an Indian does is in a circle, and that is because the power of the world always works in circles, and everything tries to be round." The tipi itself is a kind of tensegrity structure in which the load is shared by all the poles, a fact that was surely obvious to the inhabitants.

The wheel also points us toward systemic, whole-tribe wisdom, a view famously described by anthropologist Gregory Bateson. Bateson spent much of his career studying everyday life in the villages of Bali, an island and province of Indonesia. He concluded that these villages owed their social cohesion and functioning to an approach he called "nonmaximizing." These traditions discouraged villagers from focusing on any one goal at the risk of compromising others. For example, villagers balanced their traditional sense of frugality with occasional displays of conspicuous spending, thus holding competitiveness and inequality in check. As Bateson concluded, "the continued existence of complex interactive systems depends on preventing the maximization of any variable." In other words, native people looked for the spokes in their world to be roughly equal in length, strength, and tension. Obviously, this kind of systemic wisdom stands in marked contrast to the hyperbolic, maximizing tendencies that are so popular in our modern world.

Similarly, anthropologist Christopher Boehm suggested that hunter-gatherers maintained equality through a practice he labeled "reverse dominance." In a standard hierarchy, a few individuals dominate the many. But in a system of reverse dominance, the many act in unison to deflate the ego of anyone who tries to dominate them. In this kind of system, people use a number of leveling mechanisms to ensure the "domination of leaders by their own followers." In Japanese society, people sometimes say, "The nail that sticks up must be hammered down." In other words, we aren't going to tolerate any big egos in our midst. We are a wheel.

In traditional hunter-gatherer societies, people go out of their way not to appear bigger than they are. Imagine the scene when a hunting party returns to camp. A hunter has made a good kill of a large, meaty animal, but rather than bragging, he makes sure to minimize his accomplishment, a practice known as "dishonoring the meat." He understates the size and importance of his kill and calls it, in all sincerity, "a poor kill." This practice stands in marked contrast to modern cultures in which self-promotion is not only considered acceptable, but is celebrated as a path to advancement and success.

Our interest in integration naturally leads us into the study of whole systems, but unfortunately, most of us are untrained in this art. In fact, many of us are anti-trained. We are massively educated in specializations and single disciplines. We are taught to focus our intelligence on a single spoke and keep it there for years, even decades. In many circles of modern life, the rewards go to monomaniacs, individuals who develop impressive one-dimensional powers at the expense of whole-life balance and multidisciplinary wisdom. In fact, many of us are paid specifically to look at one thing and one thing only. As many of us might well put it, "The totality of the wheel is not a part of my job description."

But this view is no longer tenable. Specializations give us impressive knowledge and power, but they are also beginning to look increasingly suspect, even pathological. In fields as diverse as medicine, education, environmental science, and public health, mono-disciplinary perspectives now appear fragmented, distracting, and potentially dangerous.

You don't need to be a mechanical engineer to know that a single-spoke bicycle wheel is in serious danger. Even if that one spoke is perfectly rigid, strong, and flexible, all it takes to destroy the wheel is a minor flaw. In this sense, the wheel is fragile and at considerable risk. To make things work, specialists must pin their hopes on the assumption that other people are keeping their own spokes in fine tune. But this is a big, dangerous assumption. Who's to say whether people on the other side of campus, on the other side of town, or the other side of the world are holding up their end of things? Unless we make intentional efforts at cross-disciplinary communication, things can go wildly astray.

To be sure, some organizations make the effort to keep all the players working in harmony. But top-down, command-and-control efforts have their limitations. And besides, this is not how tensegrity works. The idea is to embed a holistic sense of attention in everyone. Take care of your spoke to be sure, but always cross-check against the whole. If everyone does this, the wheel runs smooth.

This systems-level view also shows us the value of a liberal, multidisciplinary education. Ideally, the student should try to know a little bit about all the spokes and how they fit together. Sadly, this perspective is becoming increasingly rare in modern education, as more and more students lunge for the specialized knowledge that will give them an edge in the job market. From a holistic view, this is a worrisome trend.

Likewise, our wheel also tells us that simple solutions are unlikely to succeed when dealing with complex systems. To be sure, sometimes we get lucky. A turn of the wrench in the right place and the whole wheel comes back into alignment. But in most cases, the problem involves multiple spokes that demand their own adjustments and readjustments.

In times of stress, it's easy to imagine that simple fixes will correct big, systemic problems. Politicians offer simplistic cures for what ails us, and we eat it up. "Build a wall!" "Cancel a treaty!" "Repeal a program!" These adolescent "solutions" are offered without even a nod to interdependence. People accept them at face value because it's easier than doing the actual work of balancing the total system. But in the end, these simplistic proposals are destined to fail. Any time we ignore the complexity of the whole, we put ourselves at risk.

Our bike wheel model would make perfect sense to Cornell University psychologist Robert Sternberg. For Sternberg, wisdom is all about balance. A wise person is able to balance the short term with the long term, self-interest with the interests of others, while considering all the options—adapting to the current situation, trying to shape it, or looking for a new situation. In other words, wisdom is all about adjusting the totality of the system, staying alert for imbalances between spokes. Intelligence helps, but it's really kind of a side show. In fact, intelligence without systemic wisdom may just as well make things worse. As most of us have discovered, it's entirely possible to be really smart in foolish ways.

our wobbly wheel

It goes without saying that the wheel of our modern world is seriously out of balance. We see it in our politics, and we feel it in our bodies and our hearts. Some spokes are so tight as to be near the breaking point, while others provide no support whatsoever. And mismatch makes everything more difficult. Ancient bodies and brains, modern culture, disruptive technologies, each pulling in different directions. The wheel is not only out of round, it's also accelerating. This is a recipe for disaster.

There are plenty of imbalances in the wheel of modernity, but the most obvious is social and wealth inequality. The statistics are becoming iconic. In January 2017, a report by the charity Oxfam found that eight men now hold as much wealth as the 3.6 billion people who make up the world's poorest half. The upper 1 percent of Americans are now taking in nearly a quarter of the nation's income every year. The billionaires who make up the "Forbes 400" list of richest Americans now have as much wealth as all African-American households, plus one-third of America's Latino population, combined. In other words, just four hundred extremely wealthy individuals have as much wealth as sixteen million African-American households and five million Latino households.

In 2011, the unifying slogan of the Occupy movement was, "We are the 99%." The phrase was coined by economist Joseph

Stiglitz in a Vanity Fair article titled "Of the 1%, by the 1%, for the 1%." As Stiglitz wrote, "In our democracy, 1% of the people take nearly a quarter of the nation's income ... the top 1% have the best houses, the best educations, the best doctors, and the best lifestyles, but there is one thing that money doesn't seem to have bought: an understanding that their fate is bound up with how the other 99% live."

The most notable champion of this issue has been Senator Bernie Sanders: "The issue of wealth and income inequality is the great moral issue of our time, it is the great economic issue of our time, and it is the great political issue of our time ... There is something profoundly wrong when the top one-tenth of one percent owns almost as much wealth as the bottom 90 percent." The transfer of wealth from the lower and middle classes to the elite upper class is a story of a wheel on the verge of collapse.

All of this inequality makes most people nervous. Our deep tribal heritage gives us a natural social orientation, and most of us are instinctively suspicious of radical disparities in opportunity, income, and wealth. Now, a growing body of data supports this view. The 2011 book *The Spirit Level: Why Greater Equality Makes Societies Stronger* by researchers Richard Wilkinson and Kate Pickett presents the case that the income gap between a nation's richest and poorest is the most powerful indicator of a functioning and healthy society. According to the authors, one common factor links the healthiest and happiest societies: the degree of equality among their members. More unequal societies are bad for everyone within them—the rich and middle class, as well as the poor: "Almost every modern social problem–poor health, violence, lack of community life, teen pregnancy, mental illness-is more likely to occur in a less-equal society." More equal countries have longer life expectancies, better mental and physical health, lower levels of crime and violence, lower levels of obesity and teen pregnancy, higher levels of innovation, and higher levels of mutual trust.

As observers of inequality, we tend to focus on financial disparities because they're easy to measure. But at a deeper level, the issue is really one of power and control. Money is desirable because it gives us the ability to control our world and our lives. Obviously, there are plenty of complications, but in general, more money means more control. Money is really a kind of liquid power.

But power and control have powerful mind–body effects. For all animals, including humans, more control means less stress. And less stress means fewer stress-related health problems. Not surprisingly, people with high levels of power and control are far less likely to suffer from lifestyle diseases. In a very real sense, money is powerful medicine. It's no exaggeration to say that in many circumstances, money heals.

Just imagine the last time you experienced a windfall profit of some kind. Instantly, you felt more relaxed. Suddenly, you've got more control over the world and the universe just feels friendlier. Money in your pocket has a genuine anabolic and analgesic effect on your body and mind. Your parasympathetic nervous system kicks into action with a healing response and you feel great.

Now imagine the last time you suffered an unexpected financial loss. Instantly, your sense of power, control and predictability takes a hit. The universe feels less predictable and more threatening. Your sympathetic nervous system kicks into fight-or-flight mode. Cortisol flows and begins to eat away at vital tissues, sensitizing your amygdala to be even more vigilant. If your loss is repeated, the effect on your physiology and metabolism is likely to be profound. You are primed for illness.

This is where the wobble really starts to eat away at society. As the wealth gap widens, so too does the health gap. And if present trends continue, our world will split sharply into two dramatically different populations: one with superb physical health and financial power, and another with poor health and minimal if any power. When wealth flows to the upper 1%, so does power, control, and health.

This also suggests that most of our conversations about modern medical policy are missing the most essential point. We talk endlessly about the merits and drawbacks of health insurance, subsidies, medical savings accounts, co-pays, pre-existing conditions, and deductibles. But our focus is misplaced. If we really wanted to get to the root of human suffering and prevent disease from occurring in the first place, we'd spend more time talking about inequality and what to do about it. Until we do, the entire wheel is at risk of collapse.

If the wheel is going to come back into alignment, the strong will have to share with the weak. The powerful must start standing up for the interests of the disadvantaged. Goliath must start giving some of his wealth to David. Mere charitable contributions and donations for the sake of good PR are not enough. There has to be something truly substantive. And if all that fails, we'll need some Robin Hood solutions to bring the wheel back into alignment. If the strong won't share with the weak, other measures will be necessary.

whole–part–whole

On the face of it, truing a wobbly wheel is easy: Just tighten what's loose and loosen what's tight. In theory, anyone could do it. But in practice, the art is extremely subtle. The wheel master has to make fine judgments about the state of the wheel, the extent and cause of the wobble, and the nature of the offending spokes. It can take years to learn the art.

Fortunately, there is a reliable method. The first step is to establish a rhythmic pattern of attention. After all, if you're going to bring everything into alignment, you can't just focus on one single element. The wheel master must learn to shift his attention continuously, from the whole to the part to the whole.

This is precisely the approach advocated by legendary athletic coach Vern Gambetta. Often called "the father of function," coach Gambetta advises trainers to alternate their attention in a regular pattern: Look at the totality of the athlete's movement, shift attention to the suspect joint or tissue, then go back to the whole. This rhythmic pattern builds a holistic view and a superior understanding of human movement.

It's a great metaphor, one that informs every other dimension of human endeavor, skill, adaptability, and performance. But it's not just athletic training. The same advice applies to every system in human experience, from personal relationships to large-scale policy challenges. Big picture, little picture, big picture. Go from the macro to the micro, then back to the macro. Look at the whole, make a change, then look at the whole again. Repeat.

Sadly, most of us are poor wheelsmiths. By training or inclination, we have a tendency to get stuck at one level of attention or another. Some of us focus on the total wheel. Some of us focus on our favorite spoke. And many of us are paid to focus specifically on some specific feature of the wheel. But static attention compromises our ability to address and repair wobbles. You may have your eyes on some particular spoke, and you might even do an excellent job of fixing it, but how can you know how you're doing unless you look at the totality? With millions of "one-spoke experts" among us, who is watching the totality of the wheel? Our specializations give us near-perfect individual spokes, often with no relationship to one another. The most expensive carbon-fiber spoke does us no good unless it's in an integrated relationship with the others.

This whole–part–whole perspective also gives us a fresh take on how to manage our minds. In recent years, experts have told us that we need to be mindful and keep our attention focused in one place: the here and now. Our minds are prone to distraction and our attention is scattered all over the map. Above all, we must avoid multitasking. If we can keep our attention anchored in one place, we'll enjoy all sorts of health and performance benefits.

It sounds good in theory, but there's a big downside. In fact, we might just as well come to the conclusion that single-focus mindfulness is actually a recipe for disaster. The core problem is simple: When you're dealing with the really important things in human life, you're invariably working with complex, interconnected systems—people, bodies, organizations, habitats, structures, and machines. These systems are everywhere, each composed of myriad parts, working more or less efficiently to form a coherent whole. And if you want to make the entire system perform at its best, you've got to attend to the function of *both* parts and wholes. To fix anything, you've got to keep your eye on everything.

In other words, the mind must be mobile. The warrior activist needs to exercise an agile, athletic mind, one that can attend to both big and little pictures. This calls for rhythmic oscillation of attention. Every artist does this, either by intuition or by training. Don't get stuck at one level of resolution. Zoom in, zoom out, then repeat.

Our problem is not multitasking; our problem is trying to work in wildly different domains at the same time. For example, cooking a meal inevitably means shifting your attention from one ingredient and process to another. In fact, multitasking is essential to success. The skillful cook focuses on the whole meal, then a single ingredient or dish, then returns his attention to the whole. Without multitasking, the enterprise would fail dramatically.

The problem arises when we leave the primary domain and attempt to focus on some wildly disconnected task, project, or challenge. If we talk on the phone while cooking, we straddle two completely different realms. Unless your phone call happens to be specifically related to the meal in question, it's a distraction. And this is what's killing us. In our attempt to handle tasks all across our experience, we force our minds to leapfrog from one domain to another. Not only does this exhaust our energy, it also leads to more frequent errors. The solution is to focus on one wheel at a time.

Not only is whole–part–whole an effective way to true a system, it also has a soothing quality on the artist's mind and body. Rhythmic attention just feels good. When we oscillate our focus, we're confident that we're taking in the totality of the system at hand. We know where we're going, and we're not distracted by the notion that we're missing something important along the way. Given enough cycles, we're going to get it right. The wheel is going to run true.

Naturally, success lies in practice. Find some discipline or task that needs doing. Look at the whole. Now look at the offending part. Now look at the whole. Then repeat. No matter which wheel you're talking about, it's wise to oscillate. As John Steinbeck put it in *The Log from the Sea of Cortez:* "It is advisable to look from the tide pool to the stars and then back to the tide pool again."

Long Body Practices

Only by restoring the broken connections can we be healed. Connection is health. And what our society does its best to disguise from us is how ordinary, how commonly attainable, health is. We lose our health—and create profitable diseases and dependences—by failing to see the direct connections between living and eating, eating and working, working and loving.

Wendell Berry
The Art of the Commonplace: The Agrarian Essays

Today's warrior has a lot of weight on her shoulders. She takes responsibility, not just for the events in her own life, but for the totality of the world. The tribe—all seven billion of us—is in trouble, and she will not ignore that fact. There can be no avoidance, no justifications, no fancy rationalizations. She engages the realities of climate change, habitat destruction, social injustice, and all the rest. It's a heavy load, one that weighs on her mind, spirit, and body. To meet the challenge, she must take care of herself. The stronger her life, the more meaningful her work can become.

This orientation will remind many of French physical educator Georges Hébert (1875-1957) and his advice "Être fort pour être utile" or "Be strong to be useful." In recent years, this idea has provided inspiration for parkour, MovNat, and other natural training practices. Be strong so that when times are hard, you can lend a hand and maybe even lead the tribe to safety.

"Be strong to be useful" is a powerful pro-social orientation that's a big step up from our more typical, self-centered training programs. We're training hard and staying healthy, not just to enhance our own welfare, but to improve the lot of our communities. This gives us an enhanced sense of purpose and meaning.

But Hébert was just scratching the surface, and to be honest, his advice was a little vague. How exactly is our athletic performance useful to other people or society at large? Do athletic skills and capabilities really carry over to the larger challenges of our day? Perhaps we need to be more specific about what we're doing and how we might be useful. To update Hébert's maxim, we might say, "Be strong to be a better advocate for the long body."

But being a warrior activist for the long body is a powerful challenge. Ambiguity, social conflict, and uncertainty can draw down our energy fast. To be really effective, we need to be able to sustain the fight. We've got to have reserves of psycho-physical capability and resilience. If we're personally strong, we can in fact be very useful. It's not the athletic skill that makes us valuable to the long body; it's the fact that we've got a well of energy and endurance to draw upon. This is the real reason to practice health-promoting behaviors.

But that's just a beginning. Just as we say, "Be strong to be useful," we might also say, "Be useful to be strong." We train hard and practice our physical arts to benefit the long body, but in the process, we simultaneously promote our own welfare.   It's a win–win. We build our health by giving it away.

keep it positive

We begin with spirit. If we're going to succeed in sustaining our health, it's essential that we bring the right attitude to our practices. The problem with today's health advice is that much of it has a profoundly negative slant. In fact, it often sounds like the nagging of a stern moralist: "Don't sit, don't slouch. Don't smoke. Don't eat grains, gluten, sugar, or dairy. Don't expose yourself to toxic chemicals, endocrine disruptors, or electro-magnetic radiation. Don't work too hard or get stressed. Don't stay up late."

Judging from this list, health sounds like it's mostly a matter prohibition, and in fact, much of the advice that's dispensed in the name of health sounds suspiciously like a set of religious commandments. Health zealots are passionate about telling other people what not to do. If people would just follow their prohibitions, the challenges of obesity, diabetes, and lifestyle disease would simply disappear, so they say. This makes health sound like a pretty depressing proposition. As Mark Twain once mused, "...the only way to keep your health is to eat what you don't want, drink what you don't like, and do what you'd druther not."

But where did this negative attitude toward health and life come from? Surely it wasn't a central theme in the Paleo. There were almost certainly taboos: Don't eat this plant. Don't commit incest. Don't anger the ancestors. But still, most of one's energy would have gone into exploration, finding food, avoiding predation, and enjoying the tribe.

The most obvious problem with prohibition is that it tends to suck the joy out of life. Assaulted by *don'ts*, we begin to feel boxed in, constrained, and grumpy. This saps our energy and dilutes our zest for living. But the biggest downside of lifestyle prohibition is that it backfires. As soon as we prohibit something, we turn it into a forbidden fruit with powerfully seductive qualities. Mark Twain knew this tendency well. In *The Adventures of Tom Sawyer*, he described Tom's reaction when a temperance movement came to town and made him promise to give up smoking and swearing: "Now he found out a new thing—namely, that to promise not to do a thing is the surest way in the world to make a body want to go and do that very thing." Suddenly, Tom wanted to smoke and swear.

It works the same way for all the forbidden fruits. Tell me that I shouldn't eat gluten, and the first thing I want to do is cook up a stack of pancakes. Tell me that I shouldn't consume sugar, and the next thing I want to do is cover those pancakes with syrup and whipped cream. Even more to the point, I just don't like being told what not to do. I am a wild animal, a creature of the Paleolithic, and I push back against anyone who would tell me how to live.

Prohibition turns the quest for health into a battle with the forces of temptation. Like Ulysses, we feel the need to tie ourselves to the mast of the ship so that we can resist the seductions of the modern world. But this only increases our stress. Even worse, success can only be measured only in terms of things that don't happen, temptations that we don't succumb to, events and experiences that don't take place.

In this paradigm, health is nothing more than a matter of willpower and a powerful prefrontal cortex. If you've got good inhibitory circuits in your brain, you'll be able to keep your impulses in check and in turn, be healthy. But this all sounds onerous and so dull. I don't want to succeed in health and life by virtue of things I don't do—I want to actually enjoy, create, explore, and celebrate.

We'd do a lot better if we got serious about the upsides of health and life. Instead of offering up long, dreary lists of prohibition, how about offering some *dos* for a change? For example…

- Play more, especially on natural terrain

- Eat real food and enjoy it

- Go outdoors and expose yourself to natural light

- Expose yourself to challenge and risk

- Find something you love and do that thing

- Touch other people, have lots of sex, build oxytocin levels

- Find something to laugh about

- Create something interesting, valuable, and meaningful

The beauty of this positive approach is that it removes us from the battlefield of temptation. Now the focus of our attention is on the things we are trying to create; the lure of the possible becomes far more interesting than the prospect of failure. If you're in love with your art, there's no big need for willpower. Suddenly, health begins to feel a whole lot healthier.

go outside

With so much focus on diet and exercise these days, it's easy to forget the depth of our origins and our ancestral connection with the natural world. Quite literally, our bodies evolved outdoors, in wild, natural environments. Every single detail of our anatomy and physiology is tuned for this kind of experience. In this respect, we might well say that our single most important health practice is to leave the indoor world and go outside, back to the world that gives us life.

Begin by putting your body back into its natural context. If possible, put your bare feet in contact with natural terrain. Feel the sand, the rocks, and the mud. Feel the weather. Engage your imagination: travel back in time one hundred thousand years and feel what you feel. Expose your skin to the sun, the wind, and the cold. Listen for the sounds of birds, watch as the light plays across the sky. Outdoors is where the health is.

As soon as we step outside, the body begins to feel better. Most obviously, exposure to sunlight stimulates the production of vitamin D, but that's just the beginning. A growing body of evidence suggests that exposure to dirt and animals may actually be protective against a range of diseases. Encounters between the immune system and microorganisms are part of human evolution and may also protect against the development of autoimmune disorders. Similarly, some studies have found that children raised in relatively sterile suburban environments have higher rates of asthma than those raised with exposure to farm animals. Dirt, in other words, can be a form of medicine.

Unfortunately, modern humans now spend most of their time in heavily insulated dwellings and workspaces. In other words, we're living *in vitro*. This, from the Latin "in glass," is common terminology in the life sciences. *In vitro* studies are performed with microorganisms or cells outside their normal biological context, under glass and plastic. *In vitro* studies are the ultimate in isolation.

The metaphor for our lives is apt. The modern corporate gym is nothing if not a Petri dish for human bodies. It's sterile, both literally and psychically. Every surface is wiped clean by diligent workers. Machines are lined up in perfect rows, every user wired to headphones and digital displays. Walls are decorated with motivational posters and pictures of gorgeous, Photoshopped bodies. Mirrors focus attention back onto the self while pounding music punishes the senses. The Earth is nowhere to be seen. Except for the individual bodies themselves, it's completely lifeless.

Likewise, modern urban life is best described by the oxymoron, "*in vitro* living." Isolated in our personal Petri dishes—cars, houses and workplaces—we live as individual units where we suffer until something in our minds, bodies, or spirits breaks down. We know we're disconnected from the natural world, but we're unable or unwilling to do anything about it. So we stew in our stress, our discontent, and our isolation. We might well imagine that some cosmic laboratory technician is observing us and recording data on how we perform under these artificial conditions.

Scientists who work with biological organisms know full well the difference between isolation and integration. *In vitro* studies can sometimes yield interesting scientific results, but there is no reason to suppose that what happens under glass is relevant or meaningful to the real world. What happens under glass might be of value in a theoretical sense, but there's no way to know until you take the organism out into its natural habitat. Thus the general rule in the life sciences: "results obtained from *in vitro* experiments cannot extrapolated to predict the reaction of an entire organism *in vivo*."

The solution for our distress is, quite obviously, to get out of our Petri dishes and rejoin the land of the living, the land of dirt, habitat, plants, animals, sky, and water. We must make our training and living *in vivo*. For those who aspire to live fully and in touch with the natural world, we make a play on the popular toast, *In vino veritas*, ("In wine, truth"). Instead we say, *In vivo veritas* ("In a living thing, truth").

create adversity

As every exerciser knows, it's challenge that drives the adaptation in our bodies. Without some form of adversity or exposure, the body will be content to relax and maintain its current level of function. But in a highly mechanized modern world, physical challenge is rare. In effect, we are "adversity-deprived." It's no wonder that so many of us are suffering from ill health.

The sedentary nature of the modern world challenges us to do something unprecedented and counterintuitive. Now, for the first time in our history, we have to act, intentionally and consciously, to create our own forms of physical adversity. Our primal survival motivations are gone, and unless we create some authentic physical encounter to fill the void, our health and physicality will degenerate in short order.

Naturally, this suggestion comes as yet another cultural inconvenience. After all, we have spent the last few thousand years actively insulating ourselves from adversity and doing our best to promote our physical comfort. We've built entire industries and massive layers of infrastructure specifically for the purpose of easing the burdens of survival, exposure, and physical movement. But now our success is beginning to look like a Pyrrhic victory; we've beaten back the forces of nature, but in the process, we've very nearly defeated our own health.

This brings us to a paradoxical prescription: promote your health by exposing yourself to nature. Risk your body and leave your comforts behind. Make yourself vulnerable to the elements. Go farther into the mountains than you think you can. Stay out longer. Rub your body up against the world and see what it does for your health and happiness.

Of course, intentionally exposing ourselves to natural adversity is something of an unnatural act. When you evolve in a harsh outdoor environment, your natural inclination is to rest whenever possible; we're deeply wired for relaxation and comfort-seeking. As hunter-gatherers, we were great movers, but when the mission was accomplished, we were happy to head back to camp and spend the rest of the day around the fire, watching the sky and gossiping with our tribe mates.

Herein lies the challenge. Sometimes we have to go against the grain of our primal inclinations. Our abnormal, alien environment calls for what feels like abnormal behavior. Sometimes we have to expose ourselves to harsh conditions even though we'd rather not. When the lions and tigers and bears disappear from our lives, we've got to find other motivations to get the adversity and the exposure we need.

Fortunately, there are a lot of powerful reasons to get outside. Exploration pulls us with the lure of the unknown, and a primal love of the outdoors gets us out even when the conditions are less than ideal. Once we get over the sensory shock of leaving our climate-controlled cubicles and dwellings, we find our bodies adapting fast, even relishing the sensations of burning sun, driving rain, mud, bushes, and rocky trails. These elements challenge us at first, then massage our bodies in their own way. This is nature's paradoxical embrace; challenging and sometimes harsh, but nurturing in the end, especially when we circle back to the comforts of our modern life, ready to relax and supercompensate in an anabolic rebound.

move your body

Obviously, vigorous movement will be one of our most powerful and foundational practices. The benefits are familiar and scarcely need elaboration. It's safe to say that every aspect of the human body and performance is enhanced with regular movement. Not only is physical movement good for the heart, lungs, and muscular systems, it also has profoundly salutary effects on the brain and in turn, cognitive performance. As John Ratey put it in *Spark: The Revolutionary New Science of Exercise and the Brain*, "There is a direct biological connection between movement and cognitive function ... exercise is the single most powerful tool you have to optimize your brain function." If vigorous physical movement were a pill, it'd be the best-selling drug in history.

So clearly, it's time to get up and start moving. But before we begin our physical quest, it's essential that we understand the difference between *exercise* and *movement*. Recognizing this distinction will make a big difference in the quality of your experience and your long-term results.

To put it simply, exercise is a repetitive, stereotyped pattern of movement that we engage in for a prescribed period of time, or until bored or exhausted. Movement, on the other hand, is a much broader category that includes any kind of kinetic physical activity, including things like dance, gardening, physical labor, and sex.

There's an important history to consider here. Prior to the modern age, there was no such thing as exercise. Primal humans gathered, hunted, played, and danced; they got plenty of movement simply staying alive. In contrast, exercise has been part of our experience for a few hundred years at most. Yoga, martial art, and dance may well be thousands of years old, but these early forms were holistic endeavors, not exercise as we know it today.

The same distinction holds true with nonhuman animals. With the possible exception of laboratory rats on running wheels, we never observe animals doing anything resembling exercise. They hunt, gather, graze, mate, play, fight, and flee, but never do they perform repetitive movements for the sake of "staying in shape." They move their bodies for pleasure, to explore, or stay alive, but otherwise, they eat or rest.

This suggests a broader view and a new appreciation for movement in context. When we exercise, we engage in a physical specialization, but when we move, we put ourselves back into community with every animal that has ever lived. Instead of isolating ourselves in specialized facilities with specialized machines, we're sharing in a common experience with every primate and every mammal, a deep heritage that goes back hundreds of millions of years. When we move our bodies, we celebrate our kinship with the natural world and make ourselves part of something much, much larger than ourselves.

It's movement, not exercise, that keeps us healthy. Across the board, research shows that *all* forms of physical movement are health promoting. This realization leads us to a powerful general principle: when it comes to maintaining health, exercise is optional, but movement is essential. No one ever died from lack of exercise, but a lack of physical movement is absolutely dangerous to health. As long as we're getting vigorous movement during the course of our days, we might even skip the exercise altogether. Instead of setting aside big chunks of time to perform stereotyped exercise in specialized facilities, our challenge is to weave movement back into the fabric of our daily lives. If we can make our lives more vigorous in some way, our health will largely take care of itself.

In this effort, the specifics simply aren't that important. In today's world of high-performance training and athletics, it's tempting to suppose that the path to health lies in some perfect workout formula, administered by an expert. Many of us are looking for the ideal set of movements that will take our performance to the next level. But for our purposes, specializations are suspect. In moderation, they can advance our skill, but over time, specialized, repetitive movements take their toll on joints and tissues, even the nervous system. And before long, the result is injury. All of which makes sense in terms of human evolution. Hunting and gathering are inherently diverse. The hunter must adapt to a variety of terrain, plants, animals, and weather. Every hunt is different, and even in gathering, people are constantly changing their postures to adjust to conditions. We can be certain that repetitive-strain injuries were rare in hunter-gatherer societies.

So try to avoid specialization. Dive into a practice that you love, but don't linger too long. Take up another sport, try a different training practice. Avoid year-round training by taking a seasonal approach. If you like strength training, try endurance. If you love cardio, do some weights. Keep moving your movement.

Ultimately, the essential element is not the number of workouts you do or the specifics of your training. Rather, the key is your connection to your physicality. When was the last time you felt vitality coursing through your body? Is the memory fresh or is it fading away into the background of your attention? Obviously, it's not easy to maintain this connection in our modern, digital, sedentary world. Unless we make intentional efforts to close the gap, we'll drift further and further away from our true, physical nature.

As an occasional writer, I find this to be a constant challenge. After long hours at the keyboard, my body feels far away, like a pale, thin, and unfamiliar stranger. Unless I refresh my memory with frequent movement snacks, the distance between me and my physicality gets stretched into amnesia. In a very real sense, I begin to forget who I am.

So don't get distracted by the details of programs, methodologies, or training details. Instead, focus on forging an intimacy with your physical self. Do whatever it takes to feel your vitality and your wildness.

the activist workout

Of course, as connoisseurs of context, we want to make sure that our workouts fit into the big picture of what we're trying to do with our lives. There are thousands of workout programs out there that promise everything from elite fitness to eternal life, but what we're after is something that's relevant and meaningful, something that supports the health and welfare of the long body.

For this purpose, the activist workout is ideal. This program won't make you into a great athlete or turn you into a super-model. It won't insulate you from injury or illness and it won't make you live forever. Instead, this workout will give you the vitality to fight the battles that need to be fought. It's designed to make you a powerful advocate for environmental and social issues. It'll make you healthier, sharper, and more focused and in turn, you'll be more effective at the pro-habitat, pro-health, and pro-social work that we need to be doing right now.

The beauty of this workout is that you can do it anywhere. You don't need special clothes or a celebrity trainer. You won't need any special gear or devices. You won't need mirrors or high-intensity music. Likewise, you won't need any exotic before-and-after food supplements to supercharge your metabolism. You can forget about biomechanical perfection, or getting your sets and reps just right. If you've got an injury or special needs, get professional help. Otherwise, go with what feels good. The important thing is simply to get physical.

Imagine the setting: You've been chained to your desk and your phone for hours. You've been stuck in a meeting, trying to hash out the abstract details of a project. Everything is taking longer than you think, and you can feel your vitality draining away. You don't have time to go to the gym, the pool, or the track, but there's a courtyard out back where you can disappear for awhile.

So, put down the mouse and get moving. Start with running in place and take it from there. Add some variations in your steps. Wide "monster" running is fun and pumpy. Then, if you've got room, add some skipping, lateral runs, hopping and zigzags. Next add some squats. Then some reaches overhead and some standing backstroke moves. Hoist some dumbbells or a medicine ball if you've got one handy. Maybe some jump rope. Get your breath and blood moving, then go back to work.

You can work these short intervals into your life, several times per day. This isn't going to turn you into an Olympian, but that's not the point. Even one minute of running in place, repeated often, adds up to a real difference.

go wild

As we dig deeper into our physicality with vigorous movement, we begin to feel the power of the natural world as it courses through our veins. We're moved to embrace our animal nature and dive deeper into contact with land, plants, and animals. Like John Muir, Jack London, Farley Mowat, and others, we long to feel the pulse of the natural world and learn her secrets. We want to go deep.

At the same time, we begin to question some popular language in the world of health. In particular, we begin to doubt the usefulness of the word *wellness*. Where did this concept come from, and why is it suddenly so popular?

In the beginning, *wellness* came as a pushback against Western medicine and its mechanical approach to the human body. Critics declared that "health is more than the absence of disease" and advanced a new concept that was supposed to be more holistic. *Health* just wasn't good enough anymore.

But popular as it is, *wellness* is a weak concept. It can only be traced back a few decades and even at that, it doesn't have much substance to draw on. In contrast, the word *health* has powerful merit and substance. It has a vast, colorful history, full of drama, struggle, and sacrifice. From ancient shamans to Hippocrates, Galen, Joseph Lister, Louis Pasteur, William Harvey, and Jonas Salk, the history of medicine reads like one of the greatest stories ever told. But *wellness?* There's just not much there there.

The problem with *wellness* is that it's pale, and shallow. It has no claws, no teeth, no bone, and no blood. It's sterile and lifeless. Even worse, *wellness* has now been packaged as a glossy marketing pitch that's added on to a vast range of products and services. No one really knows what *wellness* is, but it has a certain look and feel that can be hawked to consumers. Slender, smiling, Photoshopped models may be *well*, but they sure aren't real.

In contrast, *wildness* has a deep and powerful history that puts us back into community with all the other creatures of the Earth. It's a powerful antidote to the domestication that pulls so many of us into sedentary living and depression. *Wellness* is a bland, indoor word. In contrast, *wildness* is a vibrant outdoor word, one that conjures up associations with seasons, textures, wind, water, animals, and vistas. The word resonates with our innate sense of *biophilia*, our inborn desire to associate with living things.

We can feel the word *wildness* at a deeply cellular level; it's our original, Paleolithic nature. In contrast, *wellness* feels like nothing at all. It doesn't inspire our spirit, our passions or our connection with the living world. When was the last time you saw a powerful, healthy animal in a natural outdoor setting and exclaimed "Wow, that animal looks really *well*"?

Wildness has heart and spirit, guts and gonads. It's vibrantly alive and unpredictable; when pushed, it might well push back. It connects deeply into human and animal history, into the very spirit of the biosphere. *Wildness* is exciting, risky, dangerous, exuberant, and in turn, erotic. *Wellness* is dull and sexually uninspiring. Do you really want to sleep with someone who is merely *well*, or would you rather sleep with someone whose heart and body is on fire, surging with animal spirits and ready to pounce?

Wellness is a low bar that demands little in the way of commitment or risk. In contrast, *wildness* is an aspiration to merge with the entirety of the biosphere and the spirit of every animal that has ever lived. *Wellness* is simply a state of being okay, but *wildness* is the feeling of being outrageously alive. It's what we feel in the midst of a really challenging outdoor workout, when all our juices are flowing. It's what we feel when our hearts are pounding, our blood is surging, muscles are quivering, when we want to quit, but we really want more. This is the feeling that keeps us coming back, over and over again.

And it's not just about power and movement; when the action is over, the wild animal relaxes completely, into a deep state of parasympathetic quiet, ease, and healing. This wild cycle is millions of years old and extremely effective. In other words, *wildness* works.

So I say to hell with *well*. I want to be a vital, powerful, loving, and exuberant force of nature, a good animal. The time has come to expunge the word *wellness* from our conversations about the body. This means rethinking every program, department, company, and curriculum that's based on this flabby, pathetic word. Most importantly, it's time to eliminate the phrase *health and wellness* from our dialogue. At best, it's redundant; at worst, it's nonsensical. If anything, we ought to replace it with *health and wildness*. This phrase will bring some life back into our practices and our programs. It will remind us of our animal nature and the original source of our health. We can live without *wellness*, but once we give up on *wildness*, it's the beginning of the end.

practice plasticity

Wildness fill us with energy, but it also leads to some highly disruptive conclusions about how we're living. As we've seen, one of the most perplexing features of modern life is the widespread medicalization of the human experience. Today, we're fast on our way to becoming a patient population. Even people who are entirely healthy are encouraged to get into the system with preventive care and regular check-ups. The phrase "see your doctor" is presented by media and journalists as a prime directive.

If you've got a complaint about any part of your body or your life experience, there's a health professional out there who will step up to help. And in this process, we actually give away much of our power and our adaptability. As Ivan Illich taught us in *Medical Nemesis*, modern corporate medicine actually poses a substantial threat to public health. By turning entire populations into patients, our robust animal nature is compromised and diluted. We become sissies.

The solution is to demedicalize our lives as much as we possibly can. Not only should we cut back on excessive use of medical care, we should also stop thinking of our bodies and our lives in exclusively medical terms. Begin by paying attention to the way that medicalization has crept into our language: "Exercise is medicine." "Food is medicine." "Sunshine is medicine." "Friends are medicine." On their own, these statements are all perfectly legitimate, but when seen in the context of the broader human experience, they reveal a disturbing shift in identity. Do we really see ourselves as chronically sick and constantly in need of medical care? What happens to the human experience when we start from an assumption of illness? Are we really so diseased that we no longer stand on our feet without professional assistance?

The problem with medicalization is that it compromises our capacity for adaptation. It becomes a kind of prosthetic, even for people who don't truly need the help. When every ailment is treated, people no longer need to fight their way through a difficult or painful experience. And when there's no fight, there's no adaptation. When the challenge disappears, the body has no incentive to reorganize itself to a higher level of function. In this way, modern medicine often deprives us of the very stimulus that our bodies need to find their own solutions.

When used in excess, modern medicine makes us weak. And for people whose health is already compromised by sedentary living, a bad diet and stress, our "healing arts" may actually be making things worse. Sometimes, our bodies do better when they're left to fight the battle on their own. The solution, of course, is to put ourselves back into contact with challenge. Obviously, this means using less medical care. It also calls us to remember our animal nature and stop thinking of ourselves as perpetual patients. Stop interpreting every sensation and experience in medical terms. Put your body in positions and circumstances where it will have to adapt.

Above all, trust your body to find a solution. Our bodies are far more adaptive than most people think. The process of adaptation is hundreds of millions of years in the making and is incredibly powerful. Not only are we good at enduring hardship, but we're also adept at engineering internal workarounds that take us to new levels of health and integration. For the vast majority of human history, our bodies have been adapting with incredible success.

In recent decades, scientists have learned a great deal about human adaptability. In particular, neuroscientists have taught us about the marvels of neuroplasticity, the ability of the brain to rewire its circuits to learn new things and adapt to changing circumstances. It's an exciting discovery, but in another sense, it's not surprising at all. Athletes have long known about adaptation in muscle and skill; they experience it all the time. And it now appears that plasticity is the rule, not an exception. Challenge the body with some kind of adverse experience and it will respond with waves of microscopic adjustments to make that adaptation possible.

And it's more than just physical tissue. As neuroscientists collaborate with meditators and psychologists, we're beginning to see that plasticity extends even into the "softer" realms of emotion, attitude, and even what might be called "spirit." We don't just sculpt tissue with use. We also sculpt our capacity for compassion, empathy, gratitude, and curiosity. The entire organism is constantly remodeling itself according to how it's used. In a very real sense, all our human capabilites are "muscular." And of course, the same principle applies even to the process of adaptation itself. Adaptation, in other words, is a skill. We get better at adapting through practice.

Obviously, we'd be fools to avoid modern medicine entirely. There are plenty of entirely valid reasons to make use of wonder drugs, technologies, and knowledge that can make our bodies whole again. But in the main, our goal should be to use modern medicine as little as possible, to shift the challenge of adaptation back onto our bodies themselves.

Of course, the decision to seek medical care can be a tough judgment call. When you're suffering a minor injury or illness, it's tempting to go straight to the health care professional and most especially, get the fast-acting substances and treatments that will make the unpleasantness go away. But there is value in fighting and delaying the medicine as long as possible. Stay away from physicians, hospitals, health care providers, and most especially, pharmacies. Keep your body in the adaptation game as long as you can.

Likewise, if you're a medical or health care professional, you might want to reconsider your approach. Obviously, you want to provide the best possible care and ease your patients' suffering, but it's also essential to teach them the value of fighting for health. Patients need to hear that their bodies are strong and resilient. You might even encourage them to use less of your products and services. It may not be a smart business decision, but it's better for people in the long run.

Thankfully, there's plenty that we can do on our own to build our capacity for adaptation in the face of injury or illness. Practice plasticity by doing new things, especially things that take you into unfamiliar and challenging domains. Avoid specializing too deeply in any one sport or discipline. Once you get comfortable in one pursuit, intentionally put yourself in some other challenging environment. Travel. Change professions. Move to a new region. Your body will make the changes it needs to make.

Not only will this approach benefit your body and your resilience, but it also has a benefit to the long body. By using less medicine, we reduce the load on our already over-burdened health care system. If everyone leaned a little more toward their own powers of adaptation, the entire health and medical system would work a lot better. This would be a win–win.

eat real food

Just as movement and adaptation are vital long body practices, so too is good eating. This might seem to be a simple matter, but today our culture seems gripped by widespread angst about what to eat and how to eat it, a condition sometimes called "orthorexia." Popular variations include: *paleorexia* (preoccupation with Paleo diets), *carnorexia* (fear of animal products), *carborexia* (fear of carbs), *liporexia* (fear of fat), *pyrorexia* (fear of cooked food) and *supplorexia* (overreliance on dietary supplements). Everyone has a reason for their neurosis, but in the end, it's all the same: a preoccupation with some particular style of food or eating.

Of course, our problems aren't all in our heads. There are in fact some truly wicked problems with our food supply and culture of eating:

Big agriculture produces an immense amount of food, and much of that food is of poor quality.

Food manufacturers intentionally engineer food products to be hyper-flavorful and addictive.

Food marketers saturate our media with nonstop images of food, stimulating human appetites around the clock.

Social and class divisions give us radical inequities in the availability of quality food: "Food swamps" in one neighborhood, "food deserts" in another.

Nutritionists, both professionals and amateur, focus intense attention on single nutritional ingredients, an ideology called "nutritionism."

For many critics of the modern American diet (MAD), the fundamental problem lies with substances. According to this narrative, our food supply is poisoned by toxic ingredients. Popular culprits include sugar, trans fats, and gluten, as well as antibiotics and hormones. If we could just convince the food industry to clean up their act, all would be well.

The critics are right, but they've also missed a crucial point. Yes, the toxic substances are a threat, but the more fundamental problem is what agriculture does to our attention, our minds, and in turn, our relationships to the world around us. Paradoxically, our problem is a byproduct of our success. Big agriculture is really good at turning habitat into calories. It's a highly efficient system for growing plants and animals, harvesting them, processing them, and transporting the final result to our supermarkets and restaurants. It does its job so well that it's very close to being invisible. As consumers, all we see is the end product, sitting there in our supermarkets, wrapped in perfect packaging, completely removed from its source. The habitat, the water, plants, animals, and people that contribute to our food supply are all invisible and abstract.

To our naked eyes, most modern food simply appears in front of us, out of the blue. Sure, we try to read labels and ask questions, but most consumers have no real idea where their food comes from. Like a rabbit out of a hat, our food just shows up. It's a magic trick, a feast out of thin air. In this sense, we really ought to classify most of our modern food as "space food." It may or may not come in squeeze tubes, but the essence is the same. We don't really know where it comes from or how it got to us. The land and the people are far, far away. Out of sight and way out of mind.

This is particularly the case with online food purchases. Even when we buy high-quality foods from reliable websites, the effect is the same. We click the "buy now" button and a couple of days later, a box appears on our doorstep. It has no apparent relationship to anything. In fact, the internet now functions as a giant vending machine for delivering space food. It's incredibly convenient, but it also makes us blind to the land and people that sustain us.

Obviously, space food isn't going to go away anytime soon. What we can do, however, is to seek out more "earth food," food that connects us to habitat and people. Earth food isn't a particular set of ingredients. Rather, it's food that comes with some kind of story, a story that grounds it to our life-supporting systems of habitat and tribe. It's food with meaning. The problem, of course, is that earth food is hard to find in the modern world.

some useful principles

So, we've got to start hunting and gathering in our own modern way. First and most important, get over the focus on single ingredients and start focusing on real food. Stop thinking in term of "diet" and start thinking about food that comes directly from habitat. Stop worrying about biochemistry and the therapeutic effects of specific nutrients. Concentrate instead on eating whole foods from natural sources. The whole food *is* the nutrient. As Dr. David Katz of the Yale School of Preventive Medicine puts it, "The active ingredient in broccoli is broccoli."

Humans have co-evolved with real food for millions of years, and our bodies are intimately, microscopically adapted to this relationship. Every detail of our digestion and biochemistry is the way it is because of our history in wild habitat. It simply makes sense to assume that real, Paleolithic foods would be ideal for keeping us strong and healthy. We are wired for real food.

Above all, learn to distinguish between real food and so-called "edible food-like substances." When in doubt, choose the simple options. Eat the foods your great-great-great-great-grandmother would have recognized and loved. Fortunately, it's easy to tell the difference: Real foods have few ingredients; fake foods have many. Real foods are unrefined or minimally refined; fake foods are highly refined. Real foods are colorful. Real foods are tasty and satisfying; artificial foods are exaggerated, hyper-flavorful caricatures of older, more authentic forms. Real foods are perishable; glow-in-the-dark foods are almost indestructible. Real foods would be recognizable to our ancient ancestors; fake foods are only recognizable when preceded by a large-scale media campaign.

The next step is to recouple food and movement. Our modern food and transportation industry has all but eliminated the need for physical exertion; it's no longer necessary to move our bodies in order to eat. The solution is to reconnect physical effort with the tangible reward of eating real food. In the simplest terms, this means do a workout, then eat. This mimics a natural pattern that sustained humans for hundreds of thousands of years. If we drive to the restaurant and then eat, we bypass the physicality entirely. A better approach is to bike to the restaurant, eat, then ride home. Better yet, walk to the restaurant. Or at least park a few blocks away.

Next, look for ways to recouple food, people, and meaning. No matter the details of your diet, remember that food has meanings that go beyond the chemistry of the food itself. Placebo and nocebo effects are everywhere; meals are stories with meaning. Nutrition is about a lot more than biochemistry; food is glue for families and communities. Culture and personal history play vital roles in our experience and our physiology. Be mindful of what you're eating, but don't fall into the trap of zealotry or fundamentalism. People can thrive on radically different diets. Find one that works for you and enjoy it.

To eat smart, you'll have to come to grips with an inconvenient fact: the typical supermarket is a nutritional minefield in which poisons and beneficial foods are presented side by side, often in bewildering combinations. The exact ratio of real food to food products is debatable, but if we start with the assumption that highly refined grains, concentrated sugars, and trans fats are toxic to human health, its easy to see that entire aisles of the typical supermarket are literally stacked against us.

So before you enter the Mega Food Palace, try to have some kind of a plan. This is not the time for the impulsive part of your brain to be taking control of your buying decisions. Don't fall into the supermarket stupor, leaning on your cart, reacting to every bright color and interesting shape that neuromarketers put in your path. Instead, go directly to the real foods, colorful foods, old foods, flavorful foods. Make your decisions before you go in and try to avoid distraction.

Obviously, you'll want to avoid high-fructose corn syrup and refined sugars. Start by eliminating soft drinks, which are best described as "liquid candy." Avoid wheat and corn products whenever possible. Limit your intake of "carbage," the highly refined, high-carbohydrate baked goods and other so-called "white foods." These goodies do little more than spike our blood sugar levels and contribute to diabetes, metabolic disorders, and quite possibly, neurological damage.

Next, try to eat from across a broad range of habitat. Look for animals and fish that eat widely, those that consume diverse nutrients from their habitats. A prime example is wild salmon: these fish eat broadly across the ocean, accumulating essential micronutrients in their tissues and bringing it back to us. When we eat nomadic animals or wild salmon, we're literally eating the bounty of immense tracts of land and ocean.

Look for foods with a high density of nutrients. A number of rating scales have been developed that rank various foods by their nutritional density. The ANDI system (Aggregate Nutritional Density Index) has been adopted by some major food suppliers and might work for you. Alternatively, you can shop by color. Foods that are low in nutrients tend to be white or nearly so, but colorful foods promise a greater variety of minerals, micronutrients and other elements derived from the soil in which they were grown. Look at your foods in your shopping basket;

if all your selections are white or pasty looking, go back and try for a full palette of color.

As for fat, it's okay. Really. The fat phobia of the late twentieth century has run its course. We now know that the dominant nutritional advice of the day was almost completely backward, and that a low-fat, high carbohydrate diet doesn't work. In fact, such a diet actually promotes the kinds of conditions it was supposed to prevent. The new understanding holds that high-quality fat from grass-fed animals and plant sources such as avocados and coconut are extremely good for health. So eat up.

It's not just what we eat, but also when. For many, the last meal of the day comes late in the evening, a practice that many nutritionists now consider a health negative. Even when given the same number of calories overall, mice that ate around the clock put on more fat. Late eating spikes our blood sugar just as the body is winding down into inactivity and sleep. This allows glucose to circulate in the blood and probably contributes to obesity, high blood sugar, and acid reflux, as well as general depletion of the body's energy.

By eating dinner early, we create a daily "fast" that allows the digestive system to rest completely each night. These fasts allow the system to completely metabolize the day's food and clear away byproducts and inflammation. This also allows the body to divert more of its resources away from digestion and back toward tissue healing and fighting infection. The consensus recommendation is to stop eating entirely after dinner. Try for a solid twelve hours between dinner and breakfast. Likewise, if you're drinking, do it early. Give your body a chance to fully metabolize the alcohol before you go to bed. Drinking late is a recipe for poor sleep and recovery.

As for vegetarian diets, this is a matter of ferocious debate, frequent hostility, and personal choice. Fortunately, we can boil down the vitriol to a few simple statements. First, eating a vegetarian diet is a superior moral choice. There is no question on this score; millions of animals are abused and slaughtered each year to produce the meat that we consume. Without question, modern industrial meat production is inhumane and eco-hostile. The carbon footprint and water footprint is enormous. In contrast, vegetarian foods produce fewer greenhouse gasses and contribute less to climate change and other forms of habitat destruction. In this sense, avoiding meat consumption is a sound ethical decision.

As for the health considerations, expert opinions are mixed. Some studies suggest a link between meat consumption and a range of diseases, including colorectal cancer and heart disease. Other research shows that the real culprit is not meat itself, but processed meat. Among the ancestral health community, the consensus among Paleo nutritionists is that meat is vital for human health. Meat has been a fundamental part of the human diet for thousands of generations; we are omnivores by nature. Our bodies need protein to rebuild tissues, organs, hormones, and neurotransmitters. We need animal fats to keep cell membranes healthy. And while it's true that vegetarians can get protein from plant-based sources, it's generally inadequate to sustain a vigorous life over the course of decades. Even worse, many vegetarians, in their effort to avoid animal products, turn to refined grain products based on wheat, rice, and corn. In this respect, many vegetarians are better described as "carbatarians" or "breadatarians." This adds up to a nutrient-poor diet and suboptimal health.

This tradeoff is excruciating. Animal products taste good and can be powerfully health-positive, especially when they're of good quality and in the right proportions. But in general, most of what's available in our stores and restaurants is morally compromised. To be sure, we can make better choices and look for meats that are humanely produced, but these are scarce and expensive. It's often difficult to know where our food really comes from and how it's raised. If you choose to eat meat, you must understand that you're probably participating in a process that's largely inhumane and planet-hostile.

Of course, we can avoid this dilemma to some degree by eating more fish, especially cold water species such as wild salmon and sardines, but no solution is perfect. If you do choose to eat vegan, do it for an ethical reason, but understand that you might be making a long-term health sacrifice. Sadly, there is no perfect answer; we must do the best we can.

Ultimately, it's important to keep our attention on the pleasures and benefits of good eating. Our current climate of fear and restriction not only takes the pleasure out of eating, but it can even backfire into stress and obsession. Diets fail because they're constructed around a negative. Instead, we'd do better to focus on the positive. Reject the "glow in the dark" foods, of course, but seek out foods that are rich and flavorful. The modern supermarket may well be stocked with an astonishing number of disease-promoting substances, but it's also bursting with good stuff, foods that will make our bodies healthier. Focus on the super-nutritious, natural foods that make your body and mind happy. When you see yourself living in a world of nutritional plenty, you can celebrate at every meal.

seek contrast

The practice of health is not a static thing. It's a living, breathing, rhythmic process. And for that rhythm to function at its best, we need highs and low of activity, a deep, oscillating pattern of engagement and rest. When we're engaged with our work or physical training, we hit it hard, with intense effort, striving and concentration. When we're taking it easy, we power way down into deep and authentic rest. This oscillating, rhythmic pattern of activity has been part of human ancestry for millions of years.

In the modern world, the most conspicuous example of high-contrast living comes from the world of performance training, especially athletics, dance, and other physical arts. Experienced coaches and teachers know that training works best in deep cycles of effort and rest. No matter the sport or discipline, the modern coach now advises his athletes or students to "train hard and rest deep." The formula is simple: challenge the body with highly concentrated striving and attentional density, then back the intensity way off into deep relaxation. This is the life pattern of the Paleolithic hunter, the young child, the professional athlete, and the high-performance amateur.

This process is effective because it's aligned with the body's ancient rhythmic nature. Anabolic and catabolic cycles of physiology and metabolism are hundreds of millions of years old. All mammals, including ancient humans, live a natural pattern of engagement and rest. They challenge the body's tissues and organs with powerful efforts in hunting, exploration, adventure, or play, then return to camp for dedicated down time, allowing the body to repair itself and "supercompensate" its tissue growth in anticipation of similar challenges yet to come. Contrast is the key to success; by striving hard and resting deeply, we stimulate the body's powers of growth and adaptation. If we follow this rhythmic pattern, even roughly, we'll develop our capabilities and our resilience.

Unfortunately, this is not what is happening in the modern world. As artificial light, 24/7 work cycles and chronic stress have come to dominate our lives, our natural rhythm has become distorted and in many cases, very nearly obliterated. Our primal sense of oscillation has been replaced by a monotony of striving, a lifestyle of continuous partial engagement that is neither healthy nor rewarding.

Several forces conspire to suppress our natural life rhythm. A hypercompetitive, workaholic culture drives us to extremes, pushing us to compromise the oscillation of our lives. Overloaded and rushed, we try to squeeze ever more out of every moment. We work a little harder and a little longer. We cut back on our rest, first in small increments, then in more desperate attempts to keep up with the action. But over time, the effort falls apart. As our rhythm becomes increasingly distorted, our powers and performance begin to fade.

The erosion of contrast begins with deal-making and brokering. We get behind in our work, and before long we're saying, "I'll stay up late," "I'll get up early," "I'll do it on the weekend," "I'll do it on the plane," and most notoriously, "I'll make those calls on the road." And of course, electronic devices make things even worse. Always-on technologies keep us constantly hooked in. As a consequence, our lives have now become flat-line efforts of partial engagement; we're never fully focused, but never truly relaxing either. Over time, we pay the price in the form of mediocre performance and a lingering sense of unhappiness.

This flat-line lifestyle kills us at both ends of the cycle. We compromise our rest, but our performance also declines, setting us up for accidents, injury, disease, and unhappiness. As we cram more and more into our schedules, we become progressively less effective, less productive, and less fulfilled. Our flat-line lifestyles lead to flattened cognition, flattened creativity, and a flattened spirit. Anhedonia (the loss of pleasure), depression, and cynicism begin to darken our days.

In the short term, flat-lining "works." We cut back on the sleep and our precious restorative time. We cut back on the soft but powerful arts of meditation, reflection, and simple time with friends and family. In both individuals and organizations, this chronic "workstyle" leads to a progressive erosion of precious neurological assets, the very resources that make high performance and health possible.

Cognitive overload makes everything worse. We scramble to keep up with today's flood of information, but we're drinking from a firehose. Overwhelmed with choices and options, we begin to lose contact with our physicality. The objects of our attention are always somewhere else, distant in space and time. This abstraction overload even affects our humanity. According to Daniel Kahneman, author of *Thinking, Fast and Slow,* "People who are cognitively busy are more likely to make selfish choices, use sexist language, and make superficial judgments in social situations." When cognition is overloaded, willpower is depleted, which leads to all manner of poor behavior and decisions.

Obviously, many of us have fallen into flat-line lifestyles of compromised performance and inadequate rest. But how do we regain our rhythm? How can we step out of our low-contrast, high-stress lives and get back into our Paleo-animal swing of high performance and deep rest? The place to begin is with the yin side of the rhythm: authentic, genuine, and deep rest.

For many, this sounds like a no-brainer: just kick back and relax. We think of rest merely as "whatever isn't work." We associate it with those activities that we typically enjoy: watching TV, playing with computers, or talking with our friends. But authentic rest is a completely different animal. To truly rest, we need to give it the time and attention it deserves. This means allowing the entire mind, body, and spirit to come to a place of quiet, without extraneous activity.

Our best role models for high-contrast living are children and nonhuman animals. Play hard, then rest deep. Lions sleep for sixteen hours a day. Bears hibernate. Dogs go wild for a few hours, then bed down for big naps. Life is just one big pow-er-lounge, interrupted occasionally by brief periods of intense engagement. This is the norm.

Of course, given the screaming, incessant demands of the modern world, authentic rest sounds like a utopian fantasy. Who has time to do nothing? But rest is not nothing; it is essential to who we are and what we can become. Far from being mere "down time" or a boring break in the action, rest is a time of crucial metabolic and psycho-spiritual reorganization. Every tissue of the body is actively being rebuilt in rest: muscle, bone, tendons, blood vessels, neurons, and entire organs are undergoing vital reorganization. Cell membranes are restored, proteins are synthesized, and neurotransmitters are rebalanced. And, crucial for performance in the modern world, memories are consolidated and frequently used neural pathways are facilitated. Learning is enhanced.

Without rest, our striving, training, and struggling in the yang phase are wasted. But with rest, our bodies, minds, and spirits can sustain high levels of performance throughout our lives. In fact, it is the depth and quality of rest that makes the difference: the deeper we go in rest, the higher we can go in action.

Rest is not an accident, nor is it an opportunistic stroke of good luck that happens to fall into the gaps between chronic action. Rather, it must be intentional and purposeful. Like exercise, food preparation, medical care and every other important health-related activity in our lives, we have to make it a priority and set the time aside.

Sleep, of course, is a fundamental element in high-contrast living and one of the sweetest of all our animal pleasures. It not only refreshes our bodies and brings clarity to our thoughts, it also revives our beginner's mind and allows us to see old problems in a new light. When we sleep well, we enjoy a sense of contrast between stale, familiar experience and new possibilities. The morning brings the opportunity for a fresh perspective and a chance to create some new solutions. Clearly, sleep is essential for navigating our personal lives and the challenges of mismatch.

Unfortunately, sleep continues to be undervalued throughout the modern world. We treat sleep as an adversary, an obstacle to be overcome by the force of will or if necessary, drugs. People who sleep are considered slackers, a point of view voiced most notably by Thomas Edison, who declared, "Sleep is a criminal waste of time."

A substantial body of research concludes that most people in the modern world are substantially sleep-deprived. Most of us go to bed too late, disrupt our sleep with artificial light, and get up too early. The consequences are no laughing matter: poor memory, increased impulsiveness, poor judgment, decreased creativity, weight gain, suppressed immunity, and increased stress have all been linked to inadequate or poor-quality sleep. According to the University of Arizona's Rubin Naiman, sleep disorders are arguably "the most prevalent health concern in the industrialized world." In 2005, the National Sleep Foundation found that 75 percent of American adults experienced sleep problems at least a few nights per week.

But sleep is not an indulgence; it is vital for everything we want to do in our lives. Sleep is a heightened anabolic state, a time for the growth and rejuvenation of the immune, nervous, skeletal, and muscular systems. Certain restorative genes are turned on only during sleep, brain function and memory consolidation is enhanced, genes promoting myelin formation are turned on, creativity is increased, and synapses are strengthened. Not surprisingly, sleep, learning and mental well-being are tightly linked.

Not only does sleep consolidate learning and memory, it also serves a vital housekeeping function in the brain. In a 2014 TED MED talk, neuroscientist Jeff Iliff proposed that sleep helps the brain rid itself of metabolic byproducts that build up during the day. During sleep, brain cells contract slightly, allowing cerebrospinal fluid to flow along blood vessels through the brain. This fluid absorbs waste products, which are then emptied into the blood stream. During our waking state, no cleaning takes place; metabolic waste products simply build up through the day, gradually inhibiting our mental and physical performance.

Among the waste products that are normally cleared during sleep are the amyloids, insoluble misshapen proteins that form deposits and disrupt tissue architecture, and in turn, metabolic function. Excessive levels of these proteins have been implicated in many diseases, most notably Alzheimer's disease, an increasingly common form of dementia. This is a scary thought. Our modern sleep-hostile lifestyle may well be a major contributing factor in the rising epidemic of neurological disorders.

Our problems with sleep began with the advent of artificial light, a trend documented in powerful detail by Paul Bogard in his book *The End of Night: Searching for Natural Darkness in an Age of Artificial Light*. As Bogard tells it, we are now suffering a very real darkness deficit. By the end of the seventeenth century, many European cities had some form of artificial light and the darkness of our nights has been fading ever since. According to the World Atlas of Artificial Night Sky Brightness, two-thirds of the world's population no longer experiences a truly dark night. Most people are so awash in artificial light that their eyes never make a complete transition to night vision. It's no wonder we have trouble sleeping.

Our addiction to light has catastrophic consequences, not just for the body, but also for our experience of living in the cosmos. When we can no longer see the night sky, we lose an inspirational sense of beauty and wonder. We no longer stretch our imaginations into the depths of the universe. We become blinded by the light, lost in the world of artificial illumination. In 1994, a major earthquake in Northridge, California, knocked out power to thousands of homes and extinguished artificial light across a broad swath of Los Angeles. Unfamiliar with the night sky, many residents called authorities to report a "bright band of light across the sky." That band was the Milky Way.

Unfortunately, the standard American sleep style is crudely binary: keep working until your body forces you to submit, then collapse into bed. Sleep until the alarm goes off, then hit the ground running and hope for the best. Repeat the process until something breaks. A more sophisticated approach is intentional.

Start your day by getting out into the blue light of dawn as soon as you can. Greet the sun and synchronize your physiology. Get some early outdoor movement if you can manage it.

In the afternoon, begin a transition into the evening taper. Modify your activity gradually and progressively through the evening. Pay attention to self-care, health, and loved ones as you relinquish your attention to work, planning, and executive function. Meditation or relaxation will increase the activity of your vagus nerve, putting you deeper into rejuvenation. Relaxing with the company and touch of family, friends, and lovers will increase your oxytocin levels and promote healing.

As the evening unfolds, reduce your cognitive activity and allow the flywheel of your thoughts to wind down. If you seek entertainment, give some thought to its tone and character; stimulating action–adventure or highly cognitive material may not be the best choice. Likewise, make a transition from "day language" to "night language." This distinction, coined by Michael Dowd in his book *Thank God for Evolution,* is simple but powerful. Day language is the language of rationality and prefrontal function. For most of us, it's the language of work. It's about calculation, planning, sequencing, hierarchy, and control. In contrast, night language is the language of myth, story, and poetry. It's softer and less cognitive.

Here we see a promising mind–body effect. As we move into the evening, we give up the day language, and in the process, calm the activity of the prefrontal brain. It has done its job for the day and there's no point in keeping it going any longer. Ease up on the executive language, the planning, and the homework, and turn your speech toward the subtle qualities of life. Reflect. Tell a story. Speak some gratitudes and appreciations. Let your words soften and your brain will follow along.

Finally, turn down your cognition as your head hits the pillow. Your work is done. Allow your mind to drift back to the Paleolithic. Imagine yourself gazing into the campfire and the deep sky overhead. If your thoughts get stuck in distraction, bring your attention back to the night sky. Allow your imagination to roam the immensity of the cosmos, just as it would have for most of human history. Your entire visual–circadian system has been sculpted for millions of years precisely for this kind of pre-sleep experience. By gazing into the immensity of the cosmos, you can leave this day behind and forget about the uncertainties of tomorrow.

meditate

Our next long body practice is to learn some stillness. This is simply sitting, observing the breath and relinquishing our grip on the self and the worries of the day. This is where we learn to let go. This is where we allow the body, the mind and the emotions to be as they are.

Unfortunately, today's conversations about meditation are inevitably colored by our cultural obsession with individual achievement. Journalists and neuroscientists are quick to tell us about the benefits we'll enjoy when we meditate: a greater sense of calm, better focus, productivity, resilience, and all the rest. In other words, meditation is considered a means to an individual end. Just as with exercise, it's promoted as a way to build a better *you*.

But from a long body view, this gets us started on the wrong foot. By continually emphasizing benefits to the individual, we simply add to our awareness of the self, and meditation becomes just another self-improvement practice. But what if it's the self that's the real obstacle?

A more sophisticated approach goes in precisely the opposite direction. Instead of meditating to build up our powers in the world, we meditate so as to relinquish our grip on the world and ourselves. This practice isn't about improving the self. On the contrary, it's about letting go. We meditate to soften our attachment to whatever it is we're holding on to. In the process, we lose our sense of self-importance. In turn, this allows us more freedom to participate with the long body.

The problem is clear: the tighter our grip on the self, the weaker our sense of continuity with the world and the greater our sense of isolation. The challenge is to get over ourselves, to abandon the relentless focus on our lives, our problems, opinions, and justifications. Meditation helps us do just that.

So we sit and focus our attention on our breathing. But before long, the challenge becomes obvious. The human mind is an unpredictable and wildly creative creature that seems to have a life of its own. It produces an astonishing array of content, images, phrases, memories, emotions, and insights. Sometimes that content is inspiring and intelligent, but other times it's disturbing, repetitive, and unwelcome. And when our minds generate things we don't like, we try to run, fight back, or attach to something else. And before we know it, we've completely forgotten about our breath.

We double down on our effort, but that only seems to make things worse. The harder we try, the more distracted we become. After a while, we get frustrated at our inability to perform such a simple act and give up in disgust. And besides, we didn't really have time for meditation anyway.

The solution, as every coach, trainer and neuroscientist knows, is repetition. It's about letting go, over and over and over again. The mind has a powerful adhesive quality to it, and given a chance, it will stick to anything that's handy. So we need to abandon our effort and just sit. Of course it's hard. As a nation of workaholics, we are trained from birth to focus, to strive and bear down harder and harder until we succeed. This is our default setting. Letting go of anything seems like the most alien behavior in the world.

But it works. When we practice reversed effort, we get better at it. We discover that we don't actually have to engage with every idea, image, word, or association that comes up. Success at letting go builds on itself, and after a time, we develop a greater sense of equanimity. When we learn to let go of the little distractions that interfere with our meditation, we find that we can also let go of some of the big, nasty distractors in our daily lives.

The beauty of meditation is that we get to experience our experience directly. We get to feel precisely what we're feeling. And we discover, after a time, is that it's all okay. We sit and observe the mind as it churns away, generating its usual output of good and bad, beautiful and ugly. And maybe we even get scared. But we keep going back to the breath. At the end of our session, we find that our fears were never realized and our anxieties didn't really amount to anything. On the contrary, we might well discover that we feel pretty good.

In essence, meditation allows us to "go home." After sitting for a while and concentrating on the breath, the primacy of the body begins to come into focus. The images, plans, ruminations, and chatter loosen their grip and all that remains is the breath. The subcortical body comes into the foreground, and it feels good. In a way, meditation is like going backward in time, back to a preliterate, ancestral world where the body was primary.

Best of all, meditation provides experiential proof that we can live with our own minds. It's a real-world demonstration that we can be still, be quiet, and do nothing. We've done it before, and we can do it again. We've proved to ourselves that we can coexist with ourselves. There is no need to run or attach or hide. It's okay to just be.

more tortoise, less hare

The goal of life is to make your heartbeat match the beat of the universe to match your nature with Nature.

Joseph Campbell

The clock is the opposite of the erotic.
Love detests the clock.

Jay Griffiths
A Sideways Look at Time

As we've seen, high-contrast living and meditation are vital practices for the warrior activist. But to make it all work, it's essential that we question our adversarial and dysfunctional relationship with time. Time is the great riddle of the modern world. We crave it, we waste it, we let it rule our lives. To medicalize it, we might say that our problem is a kind of "time sickness" or "lifestyle inflammation." Symptoms include constant rushing and a chronic, impulsive need to hurry from task to task, even when no actual need exists. Sometimes we feel pushed by external demands, other times pulled by our personal ambition. We lunge toward the future, never sitting still, never lingering. Stressed to the gills, we define our lives as emergencies and work from an assumption of scarcity. Abundance, if we think of it at all, becomes a dream of some distant, utopian future.

Needless to say, it's an unhealthy way to live. In our state of chronic urgency, we close ourselves off from the wonders of the world and withdraw into an ever-tighter circle of tasks, calculation, strategy, and management. At this level, success consists of nothing more than meeting the demands of the current crisis; the focus is on survival, not experience. If we could just master the temporal dimension of our experience, we'd be happier and more effective activists.

Of course, our modern relationship with time is a historical novelty, and a peculiar one at that. For the vast majority of our time on Earth, humans have experienced time as organic, rhythmic, and flexible. Throughout prehistory, we lived in a world that waxed and waned with nature and our subjective experience. The passage of time was marked not by the regular ticks of mechanical devices, but by the movements of planets, weather, plants, and animals. Time may have been important, but it was not tyrannical.

In fact, many native cultures had no words for time, past, or future. In his book, *A Sideways Look at Time,* Jay Griffiths writes about the Karen, a hill tribe in the forests of Northern Thailand: "To the Karen, the whole forest was a clock." Time was alive, local, bioregional, and grounded. Time resided in natural processes and living things.

We can be certain that time sickness would have been rare or even nonexistent in human prehistory. After all, relationship and context were always more important than punctuality or precision. Success in hunting and gathering depended on observation and integration with natural cycles. The hunter would never try to go faster than the speed of habitat; to hurry would be to do violence to one's relationship with the natural world.

In contrast, modern time is synthetic, mechanical, and completely abstracted from the natural world. We believe that time is an arrow with a singular direction and linear path. Our lives are now experienced as mere ticks of a clock, standardized moments that slip through our fingers with each passing second. If we "waste" time in some unproductive manner, we're losing our allotment of life experience. Sitting in traffic, standing in line, waiting for the computer to boot up: all of these experiences are experienced as losses. And life becomes a race.

The old, Paleolithic sense of time still lingers in some parts of our world. If you're in Africa, you'll hear people talk about "Africa time." When in Australia, people talk about "Aboriginal time." In the far North, it's "Alaska time." In all these cases, the speaker is referring to a slower pace and a relaxed approach to getting things done. "We thought that he'd be here around noon, but he's on Africa time."

In the grand scope of history, Africa time, Alaska time, and Aboriginal time are normal. For the vast majority of our history, people have lived with a time sense that was circular, flexible, expandable, fluid, contextual, organic, and seasonal. Time was rich, mysterious, and alive. The default pace was easy and casual. Being "on time" would only have meaning in the context of natural events. With no mechanical clocks to set the pace, people relied on nature's time cues, cues that spoke directly to the deepest levels of human physiology and cognition.

In contrast, most of us now live on "White Man's time." Our bodies and minds are tyrannized by clocks, ruled and domesticated by linear time. Events are measured, not against natural processes, but against discrete, machine-based intervals. And the consequences are catastrophic. Mechanical time removes us from the waxing and waning of nature just as surely as if we were locked indoors or rocketed into outer space. Nothing has been so destructive to the human–nature relationship as the clock.

Today we live in a world that values the speed of the hare over the wisdom of the tortoise. We love fast everything: fast cars, fast food, fast aircraft, fast computers, fast people, and instant gratification in almost everything we do. When given the choice between two identical products, devices, or services, we reflexively choose the one that's faster. We don't really know where we're going, but we're determined to get there as fast as we possibly can.

In this way, we begin to see that White Man's time is a very real threat to human health and the quality of the human experience. The constant urgency, the relentless activity, and most of all, our radical de-synchronization with the natural rhythms of the living world—these things extract a destructive toll on the human body and spirit.

Time sickness is more than just a lifestyle problem. As our pace increases, our awareness contracts. In turn, we become increasingly disconnected from the long body. The faster we go, the more isolated we become. As we triage for efficiency, we often discard the very things that sustain us and make life meaningful. We get to our destinations in record time, but we get there in fragments.

tortoise wisdom

Aesop had it right. The hare ridiculed the short feet and the slow pace of the tortoise, but the tortoise knew better: "Though you be swift as the wind, I will beat you in a race." We laugh, but then wonder. We know that the tortoise wins in the end, but what gives him the edge? And what will it take to move from our frantic hare-culture to one that's more in keeping with the ways of the tortoise?

There's one obvious solution that often escapes our hare-brained notice. That is, we do better by doing less. Once we scale back our ambitions and cut our to-do lists down to size, things start to loosen up. Our bodies and our minds begin to relax, and in the process, we become far more effective at the things we choose to do. The beauty of doing less is that it actually creates a deeper sense of temporal affluence and all the benefits that go with it. No longer are we so desperate. We can look around and study the world. We can be more selective about the actions that we take, and in this, we can be far more effective. Our actions become targeted and precise.

Naturally, this strategy takes a certain level of courage. In today's world, the pressure to take on more and more of everything is incessant. Doing less is frowned upon, and in some settings, even the appearance of being relaxed is discouraged; if your hair's not on fire, you're not doing your job. But the slowing down has got to begin somewhere.

Likewise, the Tortoise would advise us to stop with the glorification of busyness. In today's hyper-kinetic culture, many of us have bought into the assumption that "busy equals important." We idolize the entrepreneur who works a hundred hours per week, starting companies and changing the world, or the super-mom who raises a family and runs triathlons in her spare time. If we get really busy, so our story goes, maybe we'll be important too.

But this glorification of busy–important superstars is a huge distraction that obscures the fact that by itself, busyness is not a strategy for anything. More likely, it's an expression of the anxiety and insecurity that we feel inside ourselves. As one meditation teacher has put it, "We are not restless because we are busy; we are busy because we are restless." Once we learn how to relax, our busyness will begin to fade away. As a result, we'll be far more powerful in the things we choose to do.

Another powerful practice is to maintain a temporal reserve, a buffer of extra time in planning and activity. The beauty of this strategy is that it gives us a sense of affluence and in turn, puts us into a virtuous circle. When time is on your side, everything just feels easier. Beware of the tendency to "squeeze it in," which is really code for, "I really don't have enough time for this task right now, but if I rush and cut corners, I might be able to do it." This is a formula for friction at the least, stupidity and disaster at the worst. When you feel the urge to "squeeze it in," revise your plan.

And remember, everything takes longer than you think. This is something I discovered after years in the mountains. My climbing partners and I would study the route in advance and come up with an estimate of how long the climb would take. But as hopeless optimists, our estimates were always short. Even when things went smoothly, the climb always took longer than we thought. We even had to spend a few nights out, shivering in the cold and wondering how we could have been so wrong.

Humans, it seems, are simply not very good at guessing how long a task will take. So make your best estimate, then add a substantial percentage to cover your peace of mind. If the drive looks like it will take an hour, budget an hour and a half. If you do get there early, all will be well. You can spend that free time being creative.

We can also find some peace by consulting with the ancient Greek gods. *Chronos* was the god of absolute linear time;

quantifiable, regular, and of course, chronological. This is what we think of as linear "clock time" today. But the Greeks had another, lesser-known god of time: *Kairos*, the god of timing, of chance and opportunity. The word kairos refers to the opportune or supreme moment.

This distinction sheds new light on how we might relate to time and the world at large. In short, we can behave according to the regular dictates of mechanical devices or we can be opportunists, acting in the right moments as they present themselves to us. As it turns out, both skills are essential.

Chronos skills are the basic actions and behaviors that help us synchronize with the tick and tock of white, mechanical time. Here we learn to manage our tasks, regulate our behavior and master on-time execution. In chronos, the core competencies are executive function, self-regulation, and self-management, famously managed by the prefrontal cortex of the brain. We don't manage time itself; we manage tasks, which is to say, we manage our behavior. By regulating our actions, we synchronize with the linear, modern world of commerce, business, appointments, and schedules.

There is no mystery to this process: Write things down, do the calculations, track your progress, and plot your trajectories. Once you know what's happening in your world, you can speed up or slow down as conditions demand. Even better, you'll have a sense of control. In turn, this will give your body and spirit a chance to relax. Executive labor pays off; when we exercise control, the world feels safer and more manageable.

Chronos skills are straightforward, linear and easily mastered. *Kairos*, on the other hand is more subtle and sophisticated. While chronos calls for self-regulation and discipline, kairos calls for observation, panoramic attention, and opportunism. Here we're alert to context, setting, and environment. We follow the waxing and waning of the action around us, attentive for the ideal moments.

Kairos has been our normal state of being for the vast majority of history. In other words, kairos is Paleo. In a normal, ancestral environment, we're always sensing the qualities and movements of habitat and one another, always looking for the right moments to act or rest. The kairos artist is constantly on alert for sweet spots in time, moments when our engagement will be most appropriate. Even in the midst of modern-day chaos, there are always lulls in the action, gaps between the rigid boundaries set by chronos. Kairos finds these opportunities.

The beauty of kairos is that it embraces the complexity and dynamism of the real world. Chronos skills are all well and good, but the real world is messy, ambiguous and often wicked. We need the discipline of chronos to function, but we must also be willing to abandon our linear models. This art has long been recognized by military strategists who've observed, "Plans are worthless, but planning is essential."

The most obvious place to practice this *kairological* orientation is with our major lifestyle practices: exercise, rest, food, and meditation. Many of us try to schedule these activities into regular time slots, but we are often derailed by the craziness of our days. A better practice is to relax and look for openings in the day, places where a movement snack, rest, quality food, or meditation might fit in.

By being alert for kairological opportunities, we don't work harder—we work smarter. Our efforts become more ecological. They fit into context, into the flow of surrounding events. In this way, the master of kairos seems not to be working hard at all. He simply gets better results, not because of talent or relentless labor, but because of attention.

There is a time and a moment for everything. Remember Ecclesiastes: "There's a time to be born, and a time to die; a time to plant, and a time to pluck up what is planted." Likewise, Sir Roger L'Estrange in 1699: "There is a proper time and season for every thing; and nothing can be more ridiculous than the doing of things without a due regard to the circumstances of persons, proportion, time and place." So stop looking at the clock and start looking at the world.

Our sense of temporal poverty is closely related to a general sense of scarcity. We're frightened. The world, we believe, may not provide what we need. Everywhere we look, we see vital systems on the verge of collapse. Resources are tight and diminishing; we must hurry to get our share before it's too late. This perception drives us harder and harder. But this sense of urgency is driven largely by interpretation. If we were to focus on abundance, things would look and feel entirely different. If we focused on the bounty of pleasure, wealth, and wonder in our lives, we would instantly slow down and relax. There would be no need to race.

This is where we have a choice. You can choose to spend your days obsessing over the scarcities, challenges and wicked problems of the world. If so, you can expect to feel anxious, rushed, and desperate for resolution. Life will become an emergency, and your time will shrink to almost nothing. Or, you can choose to direct your attention to the beautiful adventure and the fact that we are participants in a glorious and bountiful biosphere that is rich beyond our imagining. When you keep your eye on this ball, your body will relax and time will open up.

For the tortoise, the real issue is not time itself, but our relationship with the experience of being alive. It's a matter of fear, anxiety, insecurity, and the ability to relax in the face of ambiguity and our inevitable death. The tortoise has come to peace with all of it.

If we're afraid of death and afraid of failure, we will be chronically uneasy in our skins. Uncomfortable with the now, we'll hurry on ahead into the future, just trying to get to sometime else. We'll hurry because we need to fix our insecurity, to achieve a result so that we can bolster our self-image or sooth the anxiety of impermanence. We need to achieve something so that we can feel better about who we are. And so we rush.

But it never works. We discover that the next moment is just as insecure as the last. Nothing has really changed, and the anxiety persists. Frustrated, we accelerate, leaping forward at light speed in a futile quest for security. So motivated, many of us maintain this headlong rush for years, even decades, charging into the future. Blinded by our anxiety and speed, we miss the very things that might give us a sense of peace. We only stop when we become exhausted or when we're forced to by crisis or catastrophe.

If we could simply slow down, even for a few short moments, we could find a powerful virtuous circle and an antidote to stress. Relaxation, in all its various forms, reduces our fear and anxiety, which then allows us to feel a greater sense of abundance. In turn, our sense of time opens up and we feel less compelled to rush. And because we slow down, our sensation improves; we feel more and see more of the world around us. Our actions become better informed and more appropriate to context. Errors decline. Better performance means less wasted effort, which means more time available for sensation, study, or pleasure—all of which will keep the virtuous circle moving in the right direction.

Tortoise wisdom is subtle and often invisible. The hare is always doing, striving, and moving, but the tortoise is patient. His success comes with the not-doing, things left undone, challenges left unmet, projects relinquished. Non-action creates time, abundance, and in the end, success. So remember the wisdom of the tortoise: *Omni festinatio ex parte diaboli est.* "All haste is of the devil."

be smart about stress

As we've seen, the warrior activist is up against some formidable challenges. She's questioning Mother Culture, standing up for the Earth, and taking care of the habitat and people around her. It's no easy job. She's going to run into opposition,

263

entrenched ideas, and cultural inertia. Along the way, she's going to encounter ambiguity, uncertainty, and stress, sometimes a lot of it.

This is where things get difficult and paradoxical. On one hand, stress can degrade our bodies and the quality of our lives; it can bring disease to our brains and our world. On the other hand, stress has the potential to improve our personal and professional performance, leading us to enriched lives of health, joy, and exuberance.

Of course, stress has always been part of the human experience. We've always had to contend with challenges to our survival. Hunger, predation, conflict, injury, and disease are all part of the animal condition, and in turn, the human condition. But today, our challenge seems particularly alien. Most of us are quick to describe our lives as stressful, sometimes even desperate. Surely our ancestors wouldn't have faced such an onslaught of time pressure, workplace overload, anxiety, lifestyle disease, and ecological angst as we face in today's world. Has stress always been this pervasive?

In fact, something *has* changed. Today, our still-prehistoric bodies face an unprecedented set of challenges: noise, chronic economic uncertainty, sedentary living, strange foods, constantly shifting social relationships, high-stakes bets on careers, and an overwhelming avalanche of choice. In primal environments, challenges and stressors were often acute, but they were always congruent with habitat and the nature of our bodies. Environmental challenges triggered appropriate physical and hormonal reactions. Conditions may have been challenging, even brutal, but they always made good physical sense.

In contrast, modern stressors "attack" us more or less at random and in no particular relationship to our physical heritage or habitat. The stressors we now face are increasingly time and place independent: the phone rings or the email arrives, not in any relationship to the natural functioning of our bodies or habitat, but well, whenever. This random stimulation of our stress response system is arbitrary, and our bodies are unprepared for it. Our bodies look for patterns, but in many cases, no patterns exist.

In its modern, toxic form, stress contributes to massive levels of human suffering. It exacerbates most afflictions, especially lifestyle diseases. Stress degrades the neurological assets of both individuals and organizations. Chronic exposure to stress hormones weakens nerve cell connections and the knowledge that circulates in neural circuits. And even when it doesn't kill us outright, stress robs us of precious years of life quality and exuberance. Anxiety, anhedonia, and depression are exacerbated by stress. When we're highly stressed, we stop playing and we begin to avoid new things that might give us pleasure (neophobia). Life can lose its joy and meaning.

Not only does stress degrade our brains, it also compromises our behavior, with profoundly negative downstream consequences. When stress becomes chronic we become impulsive and make poor decisions. We become increasingly reliant on habit and more resistant to new ideas. We procrastinate and miss creative opportunities. We become socially withdrawn and resistant to collaboration. In this, everybody suffers.

To meet the challenge, it's essential that we understand the autonomic nervous system, the deep wiring that controls the basic regulatory functions of our bodies, and in turn, our minds and spirits. The standard explanation always begins with a description of the two main branches: When we perceive the world as a dangerous place, the "action system" stimulates our bodies for vigorous physical movement, such as fighting or running away. Every organ in the body is put on alert; heart rate goes up, digestion is suppressed, blood pressure goes up, and glucose is released into the bloodstream. Cognition and memory sharpen. Pain is suppressed and immunity is stimulated. In short, the body prepares itself for a physical encounter with the world. This is the famous fight-or-flight response.

The repair system does the reverse. When we perceive the world as a friendly place, heart rate and blood pressure go down, digestion picks up, and nutrients are delivered to the cells that need to be patched up. In short, the body begins to put itself back together in what neuroscientist Robert Sapolsky describes as "long-term rebuilding and development projects" such as growth and reproduction. In popular culture, this is often described as the "rest and digest" response.

The two functions of the autonomic nervous system are easy to grasp, but there's one more vital point that has huge implications for how we live our lives in the modern world. That is, the actions of the two branches are, for the most part, mutually exclusive. Either you turn on the action branch or you turn on the repair-and-restore branch. Your body has to make a choice; you can't run away from the leopard and heal your broken tissues at the same time. Over the course of our lifetimes, this difference determines, in large measure, the trajectory of our health and performance. The more often we amplify our physiology to meet real or perceived danger, the less time we spend putting our bodies back together.

To make the most of stress, we also need to understand that the body's reaction to stress hormones follows a classic inverse-U curve. Imagine a graph, with a starting point in the lower left corner. At this point, stress hormones are low and we're in a state of relaxation. There are no threats or time pressures, no anxiety and no worries. This state is pleasant, but it's also suboptimal for learning and performance. A wide range of studies have shown that we actually need some level of stress and stress hormones to function at our best.

As levels of stress hormones rise, good things start to happen to body, brain, cognition, and even spirit. Metabolic fuels are released into the bloodstream to feed our attentive brains. At the same time, our brains secrete "neurotrophic factors," chemicals that actually stimulate the growth of new nerve cells, dendrites, and synapses. In this sweet spot, learning feels like an adventure. We're playfully engaged and curious, but also flexible. Our minds become athletic, powerful, and agile. Memory is enhanced; detail and meaning are easily stored away for later retrieval. Our attention is focused and engaged. We have the energy to pursue strange and wonderful flights of fancy or odd combinations of unlikely elements. Our sense of humor is up and running.

This sweet spot is a wonderful place, but if stress is traumatic or sustained, the effect begins to reverse itself. Beyond the tipping point, our stress becomes pathological. The effects are subtle at first, but as stress deepens, the fall-off becomes progressively steeper and more destructive, to mind, body, spirit, and the totality of our lives.

The erosion of performance begins with energy depletion. Our cognitive, psychological, and spiritual resources are drained, causing both greater fatigue and greater effort. Memory and learning begin to diminish, and it becomes tougher to absorb and recall new facts and material. Now we're spending more and more of our physiological reserves just to stay on top of things: We're "burning up the furniture to heat the house."

At the same time, physical recovery begins to decline. Our bodies are slower to recuperate from workouts, injury, and illness. This leads to decreased resilience, which makes us increasingly vulnerable to all sorts of stressors, even those we would normally weather without a second thought. Aches and pains seem worse than normal, and we begin to worry about the trajectory of our health.

It gets worse. Over time, chronic activation of the stress response inhibits the growth and connectivity of precious neurons, and even damages key brain centers involved in learning, memory, and impulse control. Key neurotransmitters such as dopamine become depleted, which leads to a loss of pleasure in life. This leaves us with less cognitive and emotional energy to investigate new ideas or to drive disciplined training. In turn, learning slows, both in depth and breadth.

Over time, our mood becomes increasingly serious, then grim. We become more conservative and risk averse, or impulsive. Our social behavior becomes increasingly strained and challenging. Our sense of play and humor begins to decline, then disappears entirely. We stop laughing. We stop loving life.

Eventually, when stress hormone exposure becomes extreme, we enter the dark world of disease, dysfunction, and depression. At this point, stress hormones can actually become neurotoxic, endangering neurons and even killing them outright. Chronic exposure erodes the structure and function of the hippocampus, a crucial brain center involved in explicit, short-term memory and learning. Together, this can lead to a host of neurological disorders, ranging from minor attention problems and premature cognitive decline all the way to full-blown dementia.

Even worse, stress hormones also become psychotoxic, leading to impulse control problems and substance abuse. High concentrations enhance the sensitivity of the amygdala, a brain center responsible for fear and vigilance. The afflicted individual begins to catastrophize his predicament, imagining worst-case scenarios in every direction. And of course, he will behave accordingly, with increasing levels of suspicion and paranoia.

Finally, when the stress stimulus is inescapable and endured over long periods of time, we may lapse into a condition called "learned helplessness." In this state, we begin to generalize our lack of control, even to those cases when control is in fact possible. This state is marked by a sense of resignation, apathy, and lethargy.

So what is the warrior to do with this understanding? In the popular imagination, many of us have become stress-phobic. We simply assume that "stress is bad" and look to eliminate it whenever possible. Popular books and magazines even promise to "stress-proof" our lives. But we now know that this approach is folly. In optimal doses, stress is not just tolerable; it's essential. In fact, stress may well be the best friend that we've got.

In other words, the warrior's goal is to find the optimal level of stress: the right kind of stress, in the right intensity, for the right duration. We want precision, not eradication. Fine-tune your experience. Look for the right kind of stress, in the right intensity, for the right duration, at the right moment, in the right context. This is where a coach, teacher, or trainer plays a vital role; their job is to craft stress experiences that are episodic, relevant, and of the right intensity. The more precise the stressor, the better the learning outcome.

It's also essential to know when we cross the reversal point from beneficial to toxic stress. Someday, we'll probably be able to measure this point with technological precision, but in the meantime, a better barometer is your own body and experience. Feel your position on the curve with your gut, your organs, your breath, and the activity of your mind. Listen for the subtle signals in your mind–body–spirit that tell you, "This is too much."

Likewise, be alert to feelings of pleasure. When you're in the sweet spot, things just look right and feel right. This is a place of equanimity and equipoise. You feel calm, but energized. Your time in the sweet spot is wonderful, and you may well be inclined to push matters just a little bit further. With just a little more effort, a little more attention, a little more of everything, you might be tempted to "go to the next level."

But beware. If you take on more stress, your returns will diminish. Be alert for these warning signs:

- Anhedonia (loss of pleasure)
- Neophobia (avoidance of new things)
- Perseveration (repetition of established habit patterns)
- Reduced ambiguity tolerance, extremism and black-white thinking.
- Social withdrawal and isolation; excessive focus on your self
- Cognitive distortions, especially overgeneralizing and small-picture, short-term thinking
- Physical lethargy, poor sleep quality, decreased resilience
- Irritability, "making mountains out of molehills"
- Catastrophizing; going straight to the worst-case scenario
- Decreased sense of humor and play
- Poor concentration and attention span
- Impulsive behaviors, reduced self-control
- Decision resistance and procrastination

Naturally, recognizing the tipping point is always a judgment call. Experience will help, as it will increase your sensitivity and your ability to see the trends and trajectories of your efforts. In any case, if you feel like you're going over the top, find a way to back off.

For nonhuman animals living in wild environments, the stress response is simple and literal. When faced with an authentic threat, the organism turns on the action system and acts accordingly. But with humans, things are far more interesting. The problem begins with our immense capacity for imagination and speculation. Not only do we have the ability to sense threats directly, but we also have the ability to imagine them in ways that are completely independent of reality. Mind, story, and culture are always getting into the act, interpreting the meaning of events at every turn.

Even the most casual observer of human biology can attest to the effect of the imagination on the real and tangible tissues of the body. Watch an emotionally charged movie and you can feel the physical effects in your body: your heart might beat faster, you might laugh or cry, your palms might begin to sweat. Read some juicy erotic literature, and your body is likely to reflect that passion in some conspicuous ways as well. Symbols and images, entirely abstract and lifeless in themselves, can trigger massive changes that ripple through our bodies, minds, and spirits.

Acts of imagination have very real physiological consequences. Every thought, every mental image, every muse has a downstream physical effect. The things we think, imagine, and believe can be just as powerful as actual physical events. This is why stress researchers are careful to say that the trigger for the stress response is not a threat to the organism, but rather a "perceived threat to the organism." In other words, belief matters. If you believe some circumstance constitutes a threat to your life or your status, your body will believe it too. If you believe in the safety and friendliness of your world, your body will believe that as well.

Perception and interpretation are everything in this art. If we perceive our capability to be greater than the challenge at hand, it's going to be an easy day. But if we perceive our capability to be inadequate, it's going to be a struggle, no matter the actual nature of our circumstances. Work by June Gruber at Yale University has shown profoundly different physiological effects, depending on one's interpretation. When a stressor was perceived as a *challenge*, subjects showed increased cardiac output, increased diameter of circulatory blood vessels, increased blood flow to the brain, and increased cognitive and physical performance. In contrast, when a stressor was perceived as a *threat*, subjects showed decreased cardiac output, decreased diameter of circulatory vessels, decreased blood flow to the brain, and decreased cognitive and physical performance. Even a subtle shift in interpretation can add up to big physiological and performance consequences.

Interpretation is such a powerful driver of human experience and physiology that it even affects our long-term health outcomes. In a popular TED talk, Kelly McGonigal describes a study conducted at University of Wisconsin School of Medicine and Public Health. Researchers asked two questions: "How much stress are you under?" and "Do you believe that stress is harmful to your health?" Years later, they compared death records, and found a significant difference in mortality. Those who believed that "stress is bad for you" were significantly more likely to die than those who held a friendlier view. The authors concluded:

"High amounts of stress and the perception that stress impacts health are each associated with poor health and mental health. Individuals who perceived that stress affects their health and reported a large amount of stress had an increased risk of premature death." In other words, the very belief that stress is bad for your health is bad for your health.

The deep body is extremely adept at sensing and responding to primal threats such as predator attacks, dangerous cliffs, and fire. These kinds of encounters are unambiguous and not really open to interpretation. A snake in the grass will probably get your heart racing, no matter what kind of story you tell about it. But for the most part, our human experience with stress is highly malleable to our interpretations. Depending on the frame we put around it, a stressor may become instantly larger or smaller. The story and the meaning we bring will make an immense difference in our ability to tolerate stress. As Nietzsche famously put it, "He who has a why to live can endure almost any how." Or, we might say today, "He who has a why to live can tolerate almost any stressor." A small "why" leaves us vulnerable to every passing stressor, but a big "why" can carry us through all sorts of calamities and adversity.

We might well say that having a big "why" is an essential element in health, far more so than our conventional prescriptions for diet and exercise. Likewise, we might wonder why physicians and other health providers rarely ask us about our "why." Biomedical evaluation is all well and good, but without having a sense of a patient's driving purpose, the physician can have no idea of his patient's resilience or psycho-physical vitality. In the larger scheme of things, "why" might well be more important to the course of a patient's life than his or her blood pressure or test results.

Fortunately, big health and the long body give us a built-in sense of meaning and purpose, and in turn, an extremely powerful antidote to stress. As we know, one of the biggest stressors in human life is the sense of being alone and isolated. Some of us like our solitude, but in general, most of us will go out of our way to avoid the feelings of being separate and apart from the tribe. This is an ancient, deep, and powerful need.

But our culture drives us precisely in the wrong direction. We go to great lengths to promote individuality. We're encouraged to adopt an independent view of ourselves. Not only do we view the individual as the fundamental unit of humanity, but we evaluate individuals at every turn and set people against one another with relentless competition. In short, we promote the sense of self.

But this backfires dramatically. The more we think of ourselves as independent beings isolated from the world around us, the more anxious we become. Attention to the self distances us from the wider world of habitat and people. This sets up a vicious cycle: the more we attend to self, the more isolated we feel, the more stress we experience. In this respect, we might well come to the conclusion that modern culture is a kind of factory for stress.

In contrast, the long body orientation goes in precisely the opposite direction. By reframing our experience to be more continuous with the biosphere and our social community, we become integrated with a bigger whole. The stress of being alone diminishes. As we learn to relinquish our death grip on the self, we begin to understand that we're really a part of the most amazing family. When you embrace your participation in the long body, you're never truly alone.

live an alpine style

Health is about our minds and bodies to be sure, but it's also about the things we own. Our possessions can cause us stress or they can make our lives richer and more meaningful. Fine-tuning this relationship is an essential long body practice.

As most of us now realize, our modern practice of unrestrained consumption is not only bad for the planet; it also fails to make us happy. Many of us feel overwhelmed by our stuff. Our houses are filled with possessions that must constantly be managed, sorted, cleaned, upgraded, repaired, and replaced. Increasingly, we are tyrannized by our possessions. The things we own end up owning us.

One way out of this materialistic trap comes from the world of mountain climbing, a world in which it's essential to have a good relationship with your gear. In the early years of mountaineering, all climbing was done in "expedition style." The first Everest climbers literally needed tons of gear to get up the mountain. It took months to plan an expedition, secure the necessary material, and transport it all to base camp. From there, teams of climbers and sherpas would establish a series of camps up the mountain, climbing higher and positioning themselves for the final push to the summit. Climbers often fixed thousands of feet of rope up the mountain to protect the route and facilitate the hauling of loads.

This expedition strategy was sometimes successful, but there were serious drawbacks. Climbers spent most of their time hauling loads, and worse, expedition tactics eliminated much of the uncertainty of the climb. The essential ambiguity of the experience was compromised. After all, if you throw enough gear and labor at the mountain, it will eventually succumb. This turns climbing into a work project. Even if you do make the summit, the achievement leaves something to be desired.

But then the game changed. Equipment improved. Boots, crampons, tents, cooking gear, and clothing got lighter and more functional. Suddenly, it became possible to climb the mountain in a new way. No longer would climbers need to establish camps or fixed ropes. They could simply climb the mountain in a single push. This came to be called "alpine style."

Alpine style was the approach famously advocated by Yvon Chouinard, the founder of Patagonia. For Chouinard, the goal was to design beautiful, well-crafted tools and clothing to deepen the alpine experience and reduce the impact. As he famously put it, "He who dies with the least toys wins. Because the more you know, the less you need."

The beauty of alpine style soon became obvious to climbers around the world. This was a purer form of engagement. Less work, more sport. Alpine style stimulated the imagination and put climbers in direct contact with the ambiguity of experience. No longer protected by miles of fixed rope and numerous camps, climbers were fully exposed to the dangers and the beauty of the route. They were forced to rely on their own skills, fitness, and wits.

This was a powerful win–win. There's pride in designing and crafting simple, high-quality tools. There's joy in owning them and using them. And even when they're eclipsed by new forms, they still retain some character, story, and meaning. Minimalism is an incredibly valuable metaphor for our time, and a practical answer to the problem of consumerism. It teaches us how to own things. It teaches us to look for quality and simplicity, to value what we own and reject the voices that are constantly shouting at us to buy more.

It's a process of creative subtraction. While expedition style asks, "How much stuff can we take with us?" alpine style asks, "How light can we go? Do we really need this extra stuff? Can we put ourselves into direct contact with the experience we seek? If in doubt, throw it out, give it away, fix it, or recycle it. Go light to go long. Less is the new more.

break the spell

There is something very close to psychopathic about the intrusion of the computer into every conceivable aspect of human affairs.

Neil Postman
Teaching as a Conserving Activity

You are my creator, but I am your master.

Frankenstein

If we're ever to meet the challenge of our mismatch, one of our most urgent priorities is to create some kind of healthy, sustainable relationship with technology. As everyone knows, electronic devices have cast a spell over human life and behavior; not since Gutenberg have we seen such a radical revision of media and human culture. But in contrast to the transformation brought about by the printing press, this change has come in the blink of an eye, and it's no exaggeration to say that we are addicted.

In "The World Unplugged Project," investigators at the University of Maryland reported that "a clear majority" of students experienced distress when they tried to go without their devices for twenty-four hours. One in three admitted they'd rather give up sex than their smartphones. Once a simple tool for saving time and labor, technology is rapidly becoming our master.

The upsides of modern digital devices scarcely need elaboration. Technology advocates and advertisers constantly remind us that we can save labor and time, unleash our creative potential, and above all, stay connected. And in fact, computers and phones can be excellent tools for managing some tasks. But it's also true that our devices come with a dangerous shadow side.

The problem begins with the fact that computers and phones force us to traffic in context-free information that has no relationship to habitat, history, or setting. Messages come and go at random, but the meaning is always shallow, divorced from substance, lacking in consequence. Everything feels weightless. We spend our days chasing digital ghosts. Just click, swipe, or delete; none of it seems to matter.

Unlike conventional tools, digital devices create addiction at the speed of light. Our brains are captivated by the pattern of intermittent rewards offered by flashing lights, apps, and icons. Like Las Vegas slot machines, this pattern of occasional payoff makes our dopamine levels surge. Our brains quickly become hijacked and we crave the next fix. Our phones are casinos in our pockets.

Digital distraction takes us out of the here and now. When we cast our attention into the digital beyond, a piece of us goes missing. When we're online or on the phone, we're literally "not all here." In 2012, surveys by the Pew Research Center and Common Sense Media each reported that American teachers believe that heavy technology use is contributing to students' short attention spans. Some studies claim that cell phone use impairs drivers at the same level as a .08 blood alcohol level.

Even worse, electronic devices actually compromise our ability to make decisions. By giving us access to a planetwide data base of information and knowledge, they encourage us to keep digging, scanning, and searching, always looking for the certainty that will seal our decision and guarantee a good result. But this chronic digging becomes a kind of paralysis; we can't make up our minds, because we're always afraid that there's another nugget of information out there that will tip the scales.

We're further distressed by the fact that our communication with others now comes and goes with no discernible pattern. We send a message and wait for a reply that may return to us within seconds, hours, days, weeks, or in many cases, never. Technically, this form of communication is described as asynchronous—divorced from the normal rhythm of personal communication, mediated by the body. As human animals, we are finely tuned for face-to-face, body-to-body, real-time exchanges of meaning; the more we stretch this relationship, the more confused, frustrated, and stressed we become.

Naturally, this asynchrony also leads to monstrous levels of misunderstanding. Almost everyone has had the experience of sending an innocent email, only to have it misinterpreted at the other end, leading to a cycle of recrimination and hurt feelings or worse. Ultimately, sorting out the mess actually consumes more of our time than picking up the phone or driving across town for an authentic, real-time conversation. Electronic communication might well be described as "miscommunication at the speed of light."

The internet has now become a great global gratification machine, an impulse enabler that promises to satisfy our every desire. Browsing the internet is like being in a vast adult candy store, offering every sort of gratification imaginable. But you don't have to be a philosopher or a psychologist to know that not all impulses are worth acting on. In fact, a large percentage of human impulses are best left as they are. By enabling every urge and desire, computers turn our lives into a frantic game of compulsion, a thousand squirming impulses, all vying for attention and action.

To make matters worse, many of our new technologies are redundant to the body's native capability. For example, the human body comes wired with a social resonance circuit that allows us to transmit and understand human emotion; we have an innate, physical capacity to feel what other people are feeling. This system allows us to synchronize and coordinate emotion and behavior, a crucial factor in both Paleolithic and modern settings.

But the resonance circuit is a trainable, use-it-or-lose-it system; we become more sensitive to one another with practice. Likewise, the system atrophies with disuse. Just as labor-saving devices and transport systems have been disastrous for human muscular systems, so too will the new technologies leave us as sensory and social cripples. Technology has already degraded human communication to an astonishing degree. We are on the verge of losing our most primal sense of human connection.

And even when we do manage to use our devices in a restrained, intelligent way, there can be no getting around the displacement costs. That is, if you weren't on the computer or the phone, you'd be doing something else, something that might well be extremely valuable for your health and life satisfaction. Even worse, our always-on technology displaces our sense of wonder, away from some of the most truly astonishing features of our lives, our habitats, our bodies, and our humanity. Yes, the internet is mind blowing, but it is nothing compared to the sophistication of the body, the brain, or the natural world. Your hand, with its native network of sensory and motor circuitry, is a million times more sophisticated than the smartphone you're holding.

Looking to the future, technology has even begun to threaten our very physicality. A new wave of artificial sensors, wearable devices, smart fabrics, and personal informatics promises to revolutionize our ability to tweak, monitor, and move our very bodies. To be sure, some of these devices will be put to good use in clinical or scientific settings. But when they're mass produced and marketed to the general public, they will simply serve as prosthetic devices for people who don't need prosthetic devices. As a consequence, the body's innate intelligence will continue to atrophy.

The human body is a proven organism. For millions of years, we've used our nervous systems to feel our flesh, our habitat, our movements, and each other. We used our inborn proprioceptors, interoceptors, chemoreceptors, and other sensory organs to know our experience, our habitats, and our tribe. And for the most part, it worked. But today, we're poised to throw it all away and replace our physical intelligence with sensors and circuitry that can only tell us what we already know: that people ought to be eating less and moving their bodies more.

The consequences of this mindless love affair with all things digital will be immense. The mammalian nervous system is, without question, the most sublime creation in the known universe. New discoveries in neuroplasticity and epigenetics reveal the power of training and practice to shape our bodies and behavior. We know that transformation comes with concentrated attention and high-quality repetitions. But rather than building on these discoveries with actual experience, we are taking a wild leap away from our native capability, diving headfirst into a synthetic, disembodied future.

So what are the remedies? How are we supposed to have a healthy relationship with devices that only get more powerful and invasive with every passing moment? As with all addictions, the first step is to admit we have a problem. This much is obvious. We are so consumed by our devices that we've nearly lost sight of our deep primal heritage.

Next, we need to take back control. As with every skill, the essential elements are attention and practice. Practice turning your device off. Practice leaving it at home or in the car. Use it as a labor saver, not as an amusement. Use it as a valuable tool, but don't allow it to tyrannize your life. You have more important things to do.

Above all, give priority to people who are actually present. Face time is the gold standard for human relationship; give your full attention to present company. Be polite. If you absolutely must take a call, excuse yourself and go somewhere else.

Next, practice some triage. Strip your phone and devices of any superfluous apps and time wasters. Decide the minimum function you need, and go with that. Resist the urge to add more functions just because they're cool.

While you're at it, establish sacred spaces and times for analog, real-world experience. Protect your most precious family and social time, your most important work time. If you're going for exercise or a hike, leave the phone in the car. And be sure to program it so that it won't disturb your sleep.

Above all, identify with your analog nature, the flesh and blood of your body and habitat. Learn your body and your habitat first, before going down the digital rabbit hole. Hone your native senses. You might well be surprised how far you can go with flesh alone.

Finally, start asking questions about your devices, your screen time, and your relationship with digital information. Why do I feel compelled to check my device throughout my day? How is this device affecting the quality of my conversations, my relationships, and social discourse in general? Can I get by without a digital prosthetic? No matter your style, keep questioning your relationship with the digital world. As media critic Neil Postman put it in *Amusing Ourselves to Death*, "To ask is to break the spell."

The Power of Story

Civilization is revving itself into a pathologically short
attention span. The trend might be coming from the
acceleration of technology, the short-horizon perspective of
market-driven economics, the next-election perspective of
democracies, or the distractions of personal multitasking.
All are on the increase. Some sort of balancing corrective to
the short-sightedness is needed—some mechanism or myth
which encourages the long view and the taking of long-
term responsibility...

Stewart Brand
The Long Now Foundation

As we take in the long view of the human predicament, we
may be inclined to wonder about the exact nature of the
problem at hand. What exactly is destroying the planet? Or, to
put it more precisely, what exactly is it that's making the planet

inhospitable to human life? Or, to put it yet another way, what is it that's wreaking so much havoc on the long body?

Some might say that it's the Caterpillar bulldozer, the internal combustion engine, the chain saw, the factory trawler, and the microprocessor. Some will say it's casino capitalism, corruption, ignorance, and greed. All true enough. But when you get right down to it, the thing that's really destroying our home and our future is a story.

That's right. The story that's causing so much disease in the long body is one of domination, imperialism, self-interest, and limitless growth. It's a story of profit over people and planet, a story of short-term greed over the needs of the seventh generation, a story of power before wisdom. If we were to tell a different story about who we are and how to behave, we might well get a different result.

In *Sapiens: A Brief History of Humankind,* Yuval Noah Harari tells the story of story. Our cognitive revolution began around the campfire some seventy thousand years ago as people began sharing ideas, explanations, and speculations about their experience. Tribal elders shared their beliefs in song and poetry, which coalesced into narrative. As stories spread, humans came to rough consensus around themes of money, nation states, religions, democracy, and government. Story didn't just entertain our ancestors; it completely reorganized human society and the fabric of human experience. It probably sculpted the structure of our brains as well. It's no exaggeration to say that our lives are made of stories.

Good stories are highly contagious. And even "bad" stories, if pitched the right way, with the right emotion, can get traction. Our narratives, explanations, and interpretations travel far and wide, touching and modifying lives as they go. Stories are the raw material of human culture and experience, and our sense of meaning. We shape them, and in turn, they shape us. And they're essential for creating change. As climate activist Bill McKibben put it, "All organizing is story-telling." If we're going to have an effect on the world, we've got to tell a better story.

Unfortunately, many of us miss the deep significance. Conditioned for entertainment, we appreciate story only for its immediate, local effect on our mood and emotion. Even worse, many of us use story simply as a time-kill, a way to escape from the madness and stress of the modern world. Stories may be exciting, fun, sad, or poignant, but their value stops there. We like some stories and dislike others, but we mostly take what we're given.

Likewise, many of us are careless with our narratives. Hollywood churns out films with almost total disregard for their systemic, long body effects. Producers give us an endless series of violent, explosive action flicks with no consideration of their downstream consequences. In recent years, we've seen a growing list of apocalyptic, end-of-the-world films—movies like the Terminator series, Interstellar, Elysium, Snowpiercer, Idiocracy, Planet of the Apes, Hunger Games, World War Z, and WALL-E. This disturbing genre of "apocalypse porn" paints a vivid picture of a dying earth and humanity in crisis. As these stories tell it, our lives are on the brink, our condition is desperate, the planet is beyond hope.

Rarely do we see a realistic counternarrative of peace, wisdom, and ecological sanity. And even critics miss the larger impact. If a film is deemed exciting, cinematic, emotionally powerful, or above all, profitable, nothing else matters. No one seems to care what a destructive narrative does to our collective unconscious. Carl Jung recognized this nearly one hundred years ago: "We are on our guard against contagious diseases of the body, but we are exasperatingly careless when it comes to the even more dangerous collective diseases of the mind."

narrative activism

Activists tell stories too, but sadly, we often start off on the wrong foot. Gripped by a sense of urgency, many of us spread a disaster narrative of environmental and social catastrophe. Our hair is on fire as we rush to our keyboards to warn everyone about our predicament. As we tell it, all the curves are all bent in the wrong direction: population, habitat destruction, fresh water depletion, climate change, species extinctions, and failing governments. Rule by greedy corporations, a widening gap between rich and poor, epidemics of lifestyle disease, mass migration, and violence. All of which lead to a dark, catastrophic prognosis. Some people call this style of persuasion "disasturbation."

Forget for the moment whether or not this apocalyptic prediction is accurate. Much of it probably is. The more relevant question is, "How effectively does this story persuade?" Can we actually inspire people to better ideas and behavior by telling them that their future is nothing but a dystopia of environmental and social chaos?

It's unlikely. In fact, critics of the environmental movement have pointed to this very fact. The reason green groups fail to get traction is that they traffic primarily in doomsday narratives. End-of-the-world prophecies fail to move the needle of human psychology or behavior. Why should people bother trying to turn the Titanic if a collision with the iceberg is inevitable? Better to order up another round of drinks and ignore reality for as long as we can.

This story of imminent disaster reminds us of similar narratives that circulate in the world of public health. Experts in the field have long been distressed by epidemics of lifestyle disease and the failure of individuals to adopt healthier behaviors. Their hair is on fire too, so they warn their readers and listeners about the dire consequences of their slothful ways: "Exercise and eat right, because if you don't, you're going to suffer and die before your time. You'll be fat and unattractive. You're going to get diabetes, heart disease, and worse. You'll be a drag on the economy, and you'll go broke from your medical expenses." But of course, all of this backfires. When confronted by such a depressing, fear-based narrative, most people simply give up and head for the refrigerator. And who can blame them? Maybe if we told a better story of physical vitality, exuberance, and passion, maybe we'd get a better result.

Alex Evans made a similar point in his 2017 book *The Myth Gap: What Happens When Evidence and Arguments Aren't*

Enough? Drawing on his first-hand experience as a political adviser in the British government and at the United Nations, Evans suggests that scientists need to become better storytellers and myth makers. Well-meaning scientists have lost the ability to link the science of the planet with vital human values that we all share. To reconnect, we must tone down the wonky jargon and tell stories with passion and conviction about the restoration of nature. If scientists can't do a better job of it, they ought to let artists, theologians, and playwrights tell it their own way. For Evans, apocalyptic narratives aren't just depressing and disempowering; they also "become the perfect soil in which fascism can germinate." As people and nations fight for the last scraps of dying ecosystems, aspiring autocrats can find their way into power. The election of Donald Trump in 2016 is an obvious case in point.

So what of the long body? Can we tell a realistic, upbeat story that people can get behind? Some people are trying. Silicon Valley "visionaries" try to paint a rosy picture of a Star Trek future in which smart devices solve our problems and leave us free for leisure and adventure. But try as we might to accept this optimism, most of us remain unconvinced. If anything, the opposite seems true; the looming future of artificial intelligence and driverless cars has many of us worrying about mass unemployment and social chaos. What are seven billion people going to do with themselves when the machines take over?

The problem, of course, is reality. People might be persuaded by rosy narratives of a better future, but there can be no escaping the blunt-force fact that we are in serious trouble. Even the most conservative projections by sober scientists are disturbing in the extreme. Putting a happy face on this reality would be obscene, so perhaps it's better to say nothing at all.

There is, however, an alternative path, one that is both realistic and accessible. A big health, long body narrative points to the beneficial powers of continuity and integration. It reminds us that we can improve our health, power and happiness by connection with habitat, tribe, and culture. We become stronger as we become more whole.

In this orientation, we don't act to avoid disaster (although that would be wise)—we act to improve our lot. The beauty of this approach is that it gives us something to aspire to. Instead of living out a series of prohibitions, the big health narrative encourages positive movement, action, and ideas. It's not rose-colored, but it does offer a practical way to think and feel about our personal and collective future. As individuals, "saving the Earth" sounds like the biggest, most unreachable objective imaginable, but anyone can forge a better relationship with their bodies, their habitat, and their community.

So we look for a better story. Eat right because you'll feel better. Exercise because you'll become more resilient. Lift weights because you'll enjoy the feeling of being strong. Run some laps because you'll enjoy the feeling of sweating and breathing hard. Then, put these positive narratives together into a big health, long body lifestyle: Practice the personal health behaviors because you'll feel better. Get outdoors in nature because you'll strengthen the connection between your body, your spirit, and the natural world. Be a warrior activist because that will give you a sense of meaning.

inadequacy and disempowerment

Sadly, our modern cultural landscape is saturated with destructive, disempowering stories that suck the life out of activism. This is a story best told by Jonah Sachs in *Winning the Story Wars: Why Those Who Tell—and Live—the Best Stories Will Rule the Future*. As he tells it, inadequacy marketing lies at the core of the modern persuasion industry. The prescription is simple: Begin by telling people that they're not good enough. Create a deep sense of anxiety in viewers, readers, and listeners, then just when unhappiness is at a fever pitch, introduce a magic solution. The more profound and compelling the pain, the greater the motivation to buy. This is the standard template for marketing in the modern world.

The problem is particularly acute when it comes to our bodies and our health. In this domain, marketers do everything possible to make people feel bad about their physical condition. Just scan the magazine rack. Impossible images of bodily perfection at one end, warnings of obesity, diabetes, and neurological disaster at the other. You, dear reader, need to lose weight, get in shape, start eating right, start sleeping right, start living right, and all the rest. You, in other words, are a mess.

This story of physical inadequacy now dominates modern life and consciousness. When was the last time somebody told you that your body is perfectly okay the way it is? When was the last time someone told you that you could relax into your health, your physicality, and your life? Has anyone *ever* told you anything of the kind? It's unlikely. After all, the vast majority of messages we hear about our bodies are intentionally crafted to give us precisely the opposite impression.

It's not hard to imagine the downstream consequences of inadequacy marketing. When people are constantly told that their bodies don't measure up to some elite ideal, they'll either click the "buy now" button or suffer in silence. They'll feel depressed, and in turn, they'll reject the entire enterprise and sink back into self-loathing and bad behavior.

Our challenge is to give people a sense of power without resorting to illusion or delusion. The great news is that there's an extremely powerful narrative about the human body that's hidden in plain sight. Even better, it happens to be true. The story comes straight out of our history as wild animals, evolving in the Paleolithic era. During that 2-million-year-period, we faced incredible hardships. Our ancestors lived their entire lives outdoors, hunting animals, gathering plants, fending off predators, and walking long distances almost every day. We slept on the ground. We shivered at night and got sunburned during the day. We often went days without eating, and when we did eat, it was whatever habitat provided. We were incredibly robust.

But it wasn't just the Paleolithic. Even into the age of agriculture, frontier exploration, and industry, our recent ancestors braved incredible physical and psycho-social hardship: Clearing and planting land, raising crops and animals, digging holes, and moving rocks for weeks and months on end. Sleeping in rough shelters with minimal heat, never an air conditioner. Enduring minor and sometimes major injuries with no help from modern medicine. Fighting off infection without the help of antibiotics. We built great pyramids and great walls, sailed around the world, and explored the polar regions. People have survived weeks at sea in lifeboats without food or water. Climbers have endured subzero temperatures, extreme altitude, and exhaustion. Humans have managed to live and even thrive with every kind of diet imaginable. Combat, torture, isolation, and deprivation. We can endure almost anything. We've got it in us.

To be sure, many people perished from these adversities and many died young, but the fundamental point remains: humans are among the most adaptable creatures that have ever lived. No matter the challenge, we find a way. This is our ancestry and our heritage. In fact, your ancient, primal body is far, far stronger than you think it is. We forget this fact because we're pampered, and precious few voices remind us of our power and our resilience. But our real story is one of plasticity and adaptation. Our bodies, minds, and spirits are astonishing in their ability to survive and even thrive in the midst of extreme hardship. Whatever you may be going through at this moment, there's someone else out there who is suffering through the same kind of thing, or worse, and adapting. You are in good company.

This is where trainers, coaches, and physicians must tell the truth. We must make it clear to our patients, clients, and students that they are powerful, resilient animals, fully capable of finding their path to personal power. In fact, the vast majority of people don't need special equipment, supplements, exotic foods, and expensive experts to achieve physical health and happiness. The human body is incredibly resilient, plastic, and adaptable.

If you're suffering some kind of physical pain, know that your body is looking for a neuromuscular workaround. If you're fighting an infection, rest assured that your body is mobilizing an ancient, incredibly powerful system to destroy the microbial invaders. And if your spirit is depressed, your body is fighting that as well, seeking out meaning where it can, withdrawing from the world until the time is right to reengage. Your body and your spirit are endlessly, outrageously creative.

The problem, of course, is that this kind of self-empowerment talk is bad for business. Clients and patients who take this story to heart are likely to return to the world with a renewed sense of energy and hope for their condition. Rejuvenated, they might not return to the office, the clinic, or the studio. They might not buy expensive supplements, gadgets, or programs. Some health and medical businesses will suffer, but this is just how it goes. Telling a story of adaptability may be bad for the bottom line, but it sure is great for people.

the martial art of story

Telling stories may well seem like the most innocent of arts, but it's actually a deadly serious business. People and cultures are often fiercely dedicated to their narratives and will push back hard against stories that challenge their core assumptions and beliefs. Most of us don't like it when people start messing with our explanations of how the world works.

The key issue is attachment. As we've seen, attachment is a powerful force in human development and long-term success. Children who experience secure attachment to people and place go on to have better careers, better relationships, and even better long-term health. The beauty of secure attachment is that it gives us a safe home base from which to explore the world. But we don't just attach to people and habitat; we also attach to Mother Culture and the stories she tells. We absorb those stories into our lives and even into our bodies. And in many cases, we will fight to the death to sustain them.

Naturally, this puts the warrior activist in a difficult position. To act on behalf of his people, his habitat, and the long body, he needs to tell a better story about humanity and our life-sustaining relationships. But some people will not look kindly on his attempts to revise their native narrative. Conflict is inevitable, and we must be skillful in what we say and write. This is where we turn to martial art metaphors for guidance.

For the martial artist, there are two fundamental approaches to managing the hand-to-hand encounter: hard and soft. Either we blend with the movement of the attacker and redirect his momentum, or we meet force with force. Both of these strategies have their purpose and their place.

Aikido is a prime example of the soft approach. The method is simple in theory, but subtle in practice. In essence, the martial artist attempts to help his attacker throw himself. This art begins with sensitivity and awareness. Determine the trajectory of your attacker's movement and help him take it to extremes. Interfere as little as possible. Blend with the movement and adjust it with minimal force. Nudge him toward his own excess and help him exaggerate his own inclinations. The less you do, the better.

When working with story, the warrior activist uses the same principles. Start where people are. Listen. What are the stories people are already telling themselves? What is the tone? Who or what is the protagonist? Who are the adversaries? What kinds of values are reflected in the narrative? Who are the heroes, the victims, the rescuers? What's the trajectory of the action?

Once you understand the existing narrative, you're ready to perform some aikido. Get inside your opponent's story and direct it to get to some new conclusion. Blend, redirect, and exaggerate. Work with what people already have, then lead them to a new place, a place both surprising and yet familiar.

Consider an encounter between the human-centric and biocentric narratives of our day. Obviously, there's a huge chasm here. The human-centric narrative holds that humanity is the crown glory of creation and that all decisions must begin and end with their value to the human race. The biocentric view, on the other hand, sees creation as a vast, branching tree with humans as a single, rather insignificant leaf.

If you're a biologist or an environmentalist, you'll be hard-pressed to challenge the anthropocentric story directly. After all, this is the master narrative of Western culture and civilization. Most people are radically human-centric in their world view. This is their defining story. It carries their values and drives their attention. If you show up at the party and declare to one and all that "humans are just another species," you aren't likely to get very far. True as the statement happens to be, it's just too far outside the conventional story line. You'll quickly be dismissed as a crank. People are extremely fond of stories that put them at the center of the universe. If you diminish their stature, they'll stop listening.

So hard-core biology might not be the ideal tack. Maybe it makes more sense to point out the fact that saving habitat is actually good for people. Point out the practical benefits of ecological sanity. Point out the fact that a healthy biosphere makes for healthy people. And for those who believe that capitalist economics is what really sustains human life, give them that too. After all, there's more money to be made when habitat survives.

And speaking of money, we might take a similar approach with climate change. Instead of telling our listeners an abstract story that carbon emissions are destroying the habitability of the planet, point out the fact that rising sea levels will liquidate trillions of dollars of real estate value in coastal areas, not to mention the damage it will do to the rest of the economy. Sometimes you just have to meet people where they're at and speak in a language they understand.

Of course, the soft style approach, for all its virtues, isn't always the best choice. Just like in the real world, some statements and positions must be challenged directly. Some ideas and behaviors are so destructive and unacceptable that they must be countered swiftly and decisively. This is where we look for highly focused, karate-style responses. No blending, no appeasement, no conciliation. The key word, as they say in women's self-defense training, is "NO!" In a clear voice we say, "No, your interpretation is wrong. Your narrative is destructive. Your story is inappropriate and unacceptable."

Examples abound: Holocaust denial. Climate denial. Racism and supremacy narratives. Tyranny. Human trafficking. When these stories rear their ugly heads, we set a solid stance, engage the body, and block our opponent with maximum focus, intent, and assertiveness. These stories must stop, right here and right now. Stand up and speak out.

Of course, when it comes to telling, refining, and revising stories, the modern world is not a level playing field. We're living in a David and Goliath world. The corporate Goliath has extremely deep pockets, armies of lawyers, and media experts who are paid specifically to dominate and control their chosen narrative. It seems that an individual David wouldn't have a chance.

This is where the warrior activist turns to monkey-wrenching. We've all heard stories about activists doing their "night work," sabotaging bulldozers and other Earth-hostile machinery. But what about taking a wrench to the destructive narratives that circulate through our culture? Perhaps the keyboard is the instrument of choice. If we can tweak the narrative, we can create some change.

This is not a new idea. Ever since the first human uttered an explanation of how the world worked, people have taken issue. Writers, storytellers, professors, poets, artists, and politicians are all involved in shaping, tweaking and revising the scripts of human life and experience. Human culture is one long, never ending discussion of story, with revisions stacked on top of revisions.

But monkey-wrenching a story is not the same as editing. When we edit, our job is to clarify, reorganize, and simplify a story to better communicate the author's intent. In other words, the editing serves the story. But when we monkey-wrench a narrative, we attempt to disrupt the story at its foundations. Not only do we challenge its premises and its conclusions, but we question its very existence. We say, "This story is flawed at its core."

This is precisely the approach advocated in Adbusters magazine, the "journal of the mental environment." Founded in 1989 by Kalle Lasn and Bill Schmalz, a duo of award-winning documentary filmmakers in Vancouver, this publication uses advertising against itself. Their primary target is our corporate-consumeristic-materialistic culture. As they see it, "Advertising is an info toxin, a symbolic pollutant that targets our mental environment." In a world of constant invasive advertising, "the product is you."

Adbusters' monkey-wrenching includes a creative series of "uncommercials," "TV Turnoff Week" (later turned into "Screen-Free Week"), and "Buy Nothing Day." They've also had a hand in promoting the Occupy movement. Their anti-consumer, pro-Earth messages are routinely rejected by major networks as being "unsuitable and inappropriate."

For Adbusters, the primary tactic is "subvertising." Graphic artists take the original form of an advertisement, then tweak it to reverse and subvert its meaning. A typical example is "The American Corporate Flag," a simple graphic in which the stars of the fifty states have been replaced by corporate logos. Other notable projects target the vanity industry, asking why so many women (and men) are unhappy with their own bodies. Their monkey-wrenching message: "The beauty industry is the beast."

Political cartoonists are also expert monkey-wrenchers. By exaggerating existing narratives and recombining elements from the cultural landscape, they expose corruption and incompetence in the halls of power. In February 2017, the German news magazine *Der Spiegel* printed a cartoon by United States-based Cuban artist Edel Rodriguez. The simple line drawing depicted Donald Trump with a bloody knife in one hand and the severed head of the Statue of Liberty in the other. The point was clear. Trump's fear-based campaign against immigration poses a distinct threat to the core values he has claimed to protect. This was a powerfully disruptive act of political and cultural monkey-wrenching.

narrative medicine

The power of story operates at all levels of human experience, from the individual to the cultural to the intergenerational. Not only does it help us organize the raw materials and relationships in our lives, but it can even help overcome suffering and adversity.

In its simplest form, this "narrative medicine" seeks to give a patient or sufferer a new understanding of their predicament. Instead of attacking the affliction directly, the physician or therapist helps the patient find a new interpretation for her experience. By creating a new frame of reference, the patient can find new meaning and maybe even overcome their affliction.

Of course, this is a novel idea in the world of conventional medicine. Most health care professionals are content to adopt the biomedical orientation and stick with it. There's no particular meaning to a patient's pain. It's just a matter of flawed biochemistry, genetics, microorganisms, or physiology gone bad. We can measure it and tweak it, but it's up to the patient and maybe his therapist to find some meaning in the experience. Your interpretation of your illness is your business.

In contrast, narrative medicine actively seeks to help the patient find alternative meanings for his experience. Pain and suffering do not exist in isolation. Biomedical events are obviously real, but there are also powerful associations in the mind of the sufferer. Their pain is linked to memories, events and relationships. Suffering takes place in a living context. If the narrative practitioner can change the associations through story, the suffering might well take on a new meaning. And when the meaning changes, so too can the experience. In other words, physiology often follows story.

Critics may dismiss this approach as a cheap psychological trick, or suggest that such practices really belong in the domain of therapy. But in fact, there's plenty of solid science that demonstrates genuine medical effectiveness. As we know from our studies of the placebo effect, expectation and interpretation can drive substantial, lasting changes in physiology. Far from being a trick of the mind, this is authentic medicine.

One of the most powerful examples of narrative medicine comes to us from the world of sleep and insomnia. Until recently, most of us have assumed that the normal, healthy practice was to sleep in a single, unbroken block of roughly eight hours each night. Likewise, we've assumed that people who deviate from this standard were afflicted by something called a "sleep disorder." This assumption, it now appears, was a substantial mistake.

The new story is that humans are naturally inclined toward a segmented form of sleep with two distinct phases. In 2001, historian A. Roger Ekirch published a seminal paper, drawn from sixteen years of research, revealing a wealth of historical evidence that humans once slept in two distinct segments. His 2005 book, *At Day's Close: Night in Times Past*, includes more than five hundred references to a segmented sleeping pattern—in diaries, court records, medical books, and literature. In particular, Ekirch explores the sleeping behavior of people in the Middle Ages, before electric lighting. He found a common pattern: a "first sleep" from roughly 8 p.m. to midnight and a "second sleep" from 2 a.m. to sunrise, separated by a period of wakefulness that included socializing, quiet time, conversation, and sex. In the Middle Ages, no one expected to sleep through the night.

This pattern was the norm for much of human history, but began to disappear with the advent of electric lighting. Suddenly, people began to stay up later in the evening and the night became fashionable. As the Industrial Revolution took hold, sleep gradually morphed into the single block that we know today.

This history tells us that sleep is tightly connected to environment and culture. It also suggests that being awake in the middle of the night may not be a sleep disorder after all. More likely, it is a natural expression of human biology. As sleep psychologist Gregg Jacobs put it, "Waking up during the night is part of normal human physiology." It also tells us that sleep is flexible; there is probably no single right way to sleep.

In fact, we're now beginning to realize that individual variations in sleep patterns serve an important evolutionary purpose. This is precisely what Elizabeth Marshall Thomas described in her book *The Old Way*. In the wild, the bushmen (and women) of the Kalahari didn't go to sleep at the same time or sleep for the same duration. Rather, their sleep was staggered. At any given time of the night, someone would be up, tending the fire and keeping a lookout. Some went to sleep early, others late. People napped whenever they felt the need. There was no judgment about sleeping behavior.

Far from being a problem, this practice was actually vital to tribal survival. With a diversity of sleep patterns, someone was always awake, vigilant for predators, and ready to spread the alarm. Of course, we no longer worry about being attacked by lions in the middle of the night, but this story of individual variation does set our minds at ease. If your sleeping pattern doesn't happen to fall into line with the so-called normal standard, maybe that's just your personal variation at work. Maybe there's nothing whatsoever wrong with you or your brain. In another era, your sleeping style might have been a valued asset to survival.

This new understanding overthrows many of our old assumptions about insomnia. In many quarters, insomnia is still considered a disorder. Naturally, this label makes everything worse. People who wake up in the middle of the night must face a vicious cycle of anxiety: not only are you awake and alone with your anxieties, you feel as if there's something fundamentally wrong with you and your brain. You're awake, *and* you're diseased. The night becomes torture.

As it turns out, all this misery may well be for naught. In fact, if you happen to be awake in the middle of the night, you are probably not afflicted by a disorder at all but are simply playing out a normal evolutionary pattern. From a Paleolithic perspective, there is almost certainly nothing wrong with you; you probably would have fit right in with a tribe of ancestral hunter-gatherers.

This new-old sleep narrative is liberating. We are now free to think of our insomnia, not as a disease or an affliction, but as an opportunity. The fact that you're awake in the middle of the night is simply an expression of an ancient physiological inclination. You're awake because the tribe needs you to check the fire and watch for lions. Some of your tribe mates are still asleep, of course, but the staggered nature of individual sleeping hours means that someone will always be up, keeping an eye out for danger.

narrative medicine for the long body

Just as we reframe our narrative around sleep, we can also look for narrative medicine for the long body. This is where we reframe our experience and culture to bring *Homo sapiens* back into relationship with the biosphere and one another.

One of the most compelling reframes is bioregionalism. The beauty of this narrative is that draws us back to life on the ground. A bioregion is an area with common physical and biological features, independent of political boundaries and jurisdictions. A prime example is Cascadia, a region of the Pacific Northwest marked by a consistent pattern of forest vegetation, soils, climate, and animal populations. It includes areas west of the Cascade Mountains, Oregon, Washington, and southern British Columbia.

Of course, the bioregional approach reveals political boundaries for what they are: arbitrary divisions that have little or nothing to do with the actual facts on the ground. Forests, watersheds, plants, animals, and weather know nothing of the boundaries between, say, the state of Washington and British Columbia. Ecologically speaking, residents of Portland and Seattle have much more in common with residents of Vancouver than with cities in more arid regions to the east.

The good news is that the bioregional story gives us a positive path forward. We can't seem to agree on much these days, but we should at least be able to agree on the unity of plants, animals, weather, and watersheds that we see in our region. Even school children know that certain areas of habitat have a unified look and feel. Bioregionalism gives us a sense of place and something real to rally around.

In the modern era, the idea of bioregionalism dates back to the 1970s, championed by writers such as David Haenke, Kirkpatrick Sale, and most famously, poet Gary Snyder. But the idea is primal. Bioregional thinking has been the dominant view for the vast majority of our history on Earth. To put it another way, our current focus on arbitrary political states, regions, and districts is a recent, abnormal, and arguably insane way to subdivide the biosphere. Any child who looks at straight lines overlaid on a map is likely to wonder what they have to do with the conditions that he can see with his own eyes. I can still remember the contrast I observed when I studied maps as a child. To my young mind, there was an obvious difference between manmade divisions and the wandering, branching, and organic patterns of mountains, rivers, and coastlines.

In fact, our modern practice of drawing straight lines over living landscapes is really a kind of biocultural gerrymandering. The process is bad enough when used to chop political districts into awkward pieces to benefit political parties, but it's a thousand times worse when we use it to manipulate the biosphere for our own selfish ends. In its own way, it's really a kind of violence, another form of habitat abuse.

Fortunately, we're seeing a resurgence in bioregional perspectives. In their attempts to manage modern problems such as fisheries, water, and pollution, government and public policy makers have been increasingly forced to operate across borders. As this transborder cooperation becomes increasingly common, conventional borders begin to feel like a nuisance and an obstacle to progress.

This is where the warrior activist can do some good work. Whenever possible, try to draw attention to the unique ecology of the region you inhabit. Look for local foods and materials, and the cultivation of native plants. And whenever possible, try to redraw political boundaries to match ecological realities. The less that people use political boundaries, the weaker those boundaries will become.

Bioregionalism can also inspire us to create new forms of culture that honor that actual conditions on the ground: flags, narratives, songs, and stories that celebrate the unique natural history of our home bioregions. Use bioregional maps whenever possible. These maps show layers of geology, flora, fauna, and inhabitation over time, and are powerful communication tools for advancing the bioregional narrative.

Likewise, it's essential that we expose conventional political boundaries for what they are: an archaic, biologically bankrupt concept. Straight lines laid down arbitrarily across the land deserve our disrespect. Whenever possible, work around conventional political boundaries and ridicule them when appropriate. Bioregionalism is the way of our deep past, but it's also the way of the future. And, if modern infrastructure collapses, we may well have to think bioregionally, whether we want to or not. When food no longer comes in by truck and airplane, we'll have to really pay attention to the land around us.

We see another promising form of narrative medicine in "declarations of interdependence" that have begun to circulate through modern culture. This story begins in 1944, when philosopher Will Durant was approached by leaders in the Jewish and Christian communities about collaborating on a project of social significance. Durant proposed a Declaration of Interdependence:

> Just as independence has been the motto of states and individuals since 1750, so the motto of the coming generations should be interdependence. And just as no state can now survive by its own unaided power, so no

democracy can long endure without recognizing and encouraging the interdependence of the racial and religious groups composing it.

The text of the declaration:

Human progress having reached a high level through respect for the liberty and dignity of men, it has become desirable to re-affirm these evident truths:

That differences of race, color, and creed are natural, and that diverse groups, institutions, and ideas are stimulating factors in the development of man;

- That to promote harmony in diversity is a responsible task of religion and statesmanship;
- That since no individual can express the whole truth, it is essential to treat with understanding and good will those whose views differ from our own;
- That by the testimony of history, intolerance is the door to violence, brutality, and dictatorship; and
- That the realization of human interdependence and solidarity is the best guard of civilization.

Therefore, we solemnly resolve, and invite everyone to join in united action.

- To uphold and promote human fellowship through mutual consideration and respect;
- To champion human dignity and decency, and to safeguard these without distinction of race, or color, or creed;

- To strive in concert with others to discourage all animosities arising from these differences, and to unite all groups in the fair play of civilized life.

Rooted in freedom, bonded in the fellowship of danger, sharing everywhere a common human blood, we declare again that all men are brothers, and that mutual tolerance is the price of liberty.

In 1976, Greenpeace offered its own Declaration of Interdependence, excerpted here:

> As surely as Copernicus taught us that the Earth was not the centre of the universe, ecology teaches us that mankind is not the centre of life on this planet. Each species has its function in the scheme of life.
>
> Ecology has taught us that the entire Earth is part of our 'body' and that we must learn to respect it as much as we respect ourselves. As we love ourselves, we must also love all forms of life in the planetary system—the whales, the seals, the forests, and the seas. Ecological thought shows us a pathway back to an understanding of the natural world—an understanding that is imperative if we are to avoid a total collapse of the global ecosystem.

Still others have added to the narrative. Canadian environmentalist David Suzuki wrote a Declaration of Interdependence for the 1992 UN Earth Summit in Rio de Janeiro. It reads as follows:

This we know:

We are the earth, through the plants and animals that nourish us.

We are the rains and the oceans that flow through our veins.

We are the breath of the forests of the land, and the plants of the sea.

We are human animals, related to all other life as descendants of the firstborn cell.

We share with these kin a common history, written in our genes.

We share a common present, filled with uncertainty.

And we share a common future, as yet untold.

We humans are but one of thirty million species weaving the thin layer of life enveloping the world.

The stability of communities of living things depends upon this diversity.

Linked in that web, we are interconnected — using, cleansing, sharing and replenishing the fundamental elements of life.

Our home, planet Earth, is finite; all life shares its resources and the energy from the sun, and therefore has limits to growth.

For the first time, we have touched those limits.

When we compromise the air, the water, the soil and the variety of life, we steal from the endless future to serve the fleeting present.

This we believe:

Humans have become so numerous and our tools
so powerful that we have driven fellow creatures to
extinction, dammed the great rivers, torn down ancient
forests, poisoned the earth, rain and wind, and ripped
holes in the sky.

Our science has brought pain as well as joy; our comfort
is paid for by the suffering of millions.

We are learning from our mistakes, we are mourning
our vanished kin, and we now build a new politics of
hope.

We respect and uphold the absolute need for clean air,
water and soil.

We see that economic activities that benefit the few
while shrinking the inheritance of many are wrong.

And since environmental degradation erodes biological
capital forever, full ecological and social cost must enter
all equations of development.

We are one brief generation in the long march of time;
the future is not ours to erase.

So where knowledge is limited, we will remember all
those who will walk after us, and err on the side of
caution.

This we resolve:

All this that we know and believe must now become the
foundation of the way we live.

At this turning point in our relationship with Earth, we
work for an evolution: from dominance to partnership;
from fragmentation to connection; from insecurity, to
interdependence.

These stories of interdependence reframe our conventional view of isolated individuals and nation-states. It offers a cure for our myopia, our nationalism, our racism, our fear, and our human supremacy. A similar narrative draws our attention to our descendants in the form of a "Seventh Generation Amendment" to the US constitution, part of the Green Party agenda and the Winona LaDuke for Vice President campaign in 2000. As LaDuke wrote:

> Our proposed Seventh Generation Amendment to the US Constitution states, 'The right of citizens of the United States to use and enjoy air, water, sunlight and other renewable resources determined by the Congress to be common property shall not be impaired, nor shall such use impair their availability for the use of future generations.'

No matter your history or orientation, it's essential that we question the narratives that drive our behavior and values. We're reminded of Socrates and his legendary quip, "The unexamined life is not worth living." So too for the unexamined narrative. When we fail to question our stories, we lose our power in the world. The stories begin to tell us. Sadly, many of us haven't even bothered to question the stories that drive us. One of the greatest tragedies of human life is to wake up in old age and realize you've been fighting for the wrong narrative.

Where do you get your narrative? Is it your own? Who is telling the story, and what are their motives? Perhaps you think the story is exclusively your own and that you're the protagonist of your own drama. More likely, your life is embedded in larger, cocreated narratives that constantly course through human life and culture.

Sometimes, Mother Culture provides us with a useful, inspiring, and powerful narrative that gives us guidance in navigating the world. But as we've seen, Mom can be wrong. Her story can be misguided or misleading. We must be careful. If Mom's story isn't giving us what we need, we must look elsewhere for better narratives or craft them ourselves.

Tribal Eldership

The eyes of the future are looking back at us and they are praying for us to see beyond our own time.

Terry Tempest Williams

The more sand that has escaped from the hourglass of our life, the clearer we should see through it.

Jean-Paul Sartre

As the warrior activist matures she begins to see her work in a new light. Years of effort take on new meaning and she begins to adopt a new role, that of tribal elder. Her body isn't as strong as it once was and her skin is beginning to wrinkle, but none of it matters, because she's seeing the world from a more expansive point of view. She's working for the long body now, and her purpose is clear.

Everyone knows the standard narrative of aging in the modern world: it's one long, depressing decline into degeneration, illness, and irrelevance. Certain events are said to be inevitable: decreased physical and cognitive function, massive medical bills and possible bankruptcy, neurological meltdown, and perhaps worst of all, social and cultural irrelevance. In short, getting older is a disaster to be avoided by any means possible.

The outlook is grim, so we medicalize the process with every means available. We treat aging like a disease and conjure up all manner of treatments and substances to slow, stop, or reverse the process. Time becomes our enemy. Gripped by anxiety, we promote the virtues of "healthy aging" while experts tell us how to become a "superager." A flood of books and magazine articles tell us how to get older without, well, actually getting older. We try to stop the clock, reverse the damage, delay the onset, reduce the effects, and dampen the symptoms. What we really mean by "healthy aging" is not aging at all.

But the personal and social consequences of this narrative are catastrophic. Not only does it make us increasingly miserable as time goes by, it also drives the widespread practice of ageism. Under the influence of this narrative, we begin to see seniors as nothing more than a drag on society and the economy. Old people are a burden and an inconvenience; they become progressively less valuable to us with every passing moment. Human value, in other words, decreases over time.

This narrative is both wasteful and counterproductive. Not only does it devalue great swaths of human life; it also puts us under an insane level of stress. If you believe that your best years are your 30s and 40s, followed by a progressive decline into illness and irrelevance, the clock is going to be ticking loud and hard. Your sense of urgency will magnify with every passing year. You've got to hurry up and make something happen, because once your body starts slowing down, it's game over. Even worse, you've got to make yourself a big pile of money right now, because once you hit 50, the medical–industrial complex is going to step in and take most of it away.

Sadly, the modern health and fitness industry is a powerful enabler of this destructive narrative. Gyms and trainers are enthusiastic partners in the medicalization of aging. For every age-related insult to the human body, someone claims to have a solution. Diets and substances galore, exercise programs for every ailment, exotic treatments of every description—the list is endless. Magazine covers and websites glorify youth and sell us the promise of eternal life. According to the marketing pitch, aging is not inevitable; it's simply the failure to eat the right things and move in the right ways. If you get on a program with us, you'll never have to suffer the ravages of time.

But viewed in the context of human history, today's narrative is profoundly abnormal. In the Paleolithic, tribal survival was highly dependent on the experience and wisdom of the elders. The old ones had witnessed the cycles of weather and seasons. They'd participated in many hunts, and had seen the waxing and waning of animal life. They'd seen the tribe suffer and flourish. In this world, the words of the elders carried enormous weight. As the keepers of vital knowledge and wisdom, they were the most valuable and respected members of the community. In the Paleolithic world, human value actually *increased* over time. This is why Native Americans say, "When an elder dies, a library burns."

Tragically, we are the first culture in human history to devalue its elders. Likewise, we are the first culture in history to reject the very people who might help us choose the best path forward. To make progress, it's essential that we turn this narrative of aging around, but where shall we begin?

A good first step would be to give up our obsession with youth. Yes, there's plenty to be said for the vitality and exuberance of young adulthood, and all the pleasures that go with it. But to promote this state to the exclusion of all else makes us both blind and unhappy. The wiser course is to start taking responsibility for our role as elders-in-training. This means learning the ways of the world and sharing our knowledge with those within our reach. It is not acceptable to simply long for an easy retirement on the golf course. We must step up.

In the world of prehistory, the elders were fully aware of their role. Experience in wild outdoor environments made it clear: the primary purpose of the elder was to act on behalf of the tribe, to share their knowledge, to give away their insights so that the tribe could live another day, another year. There would have been no thought of retirement, no notion of self-pampering or hoarding. For the Paleolithic senior citizen, the primal directive was simple: give your knowledge away so that the tribe can live.

And with all due respect to the seniors in today's world, there's no escaping the fact that many older people have hitched their star to the wrong narrative. They've bought into a belief that one's senior years ought to be a time for relaxing at the second home, taking golf lessons, or touring the country in a gigantic RV. Retirement, in other words, is about pampering the self. But in the traditional native–indigenous view, this behavior would be seen as self-indulgent and antisocial. In fact, the duty of the senior citizen is to take leadership, to assume responsibility and show the way forward.

The urgency of our time is to teach what we know, to pass our knowledge to the younger members of our tribe so that they might live. So take a fresh look at your body and your life: Your wrinkles, your aching joints, and your diminished athletic performance are not downsides to be eliminated; they are badges of authority and reminders of your sacred responsibility.

The elder sees the writing on the wall. Her body hurts. Her legs don't work as well as they once did. She has trouble keeping up on the hunt, and she's seen what happens to the others who fall behind. Her days are clearly numbered. But far from being a cause for unhappiness, this is a powerful motivator. Now her energies are focused. She wastes no time with trivial gossip or amusement. She must share what she knows and do it soon.

In this respect, the tribal elder is the ultimate servant leader. As she looks out at the rolling grassland, she sees the immensity of her habitat. She feels the exposure, and she knows just how hard it is to stay alive. She worries about the state of her tribe and what it will take to keep them in the game. Their survival hangs on a thread. Has she done all she can to help them navigate the world? Do the young hunters know all they need to know about the ways of the animals, the weather, and the threats from neighboring tribes? What else must she teach before she makes the great journey?

As a servant leader, the tribal elder understands her health in a new way, one that may well come as a surprise to our modern ears. In today's youth-oriented culture, we're constantly bombarded with messages, products, and services designed to keep us forever young. Heeding this call, we begin to do everything possible to maximize our individual short body health. We focus on ourselves, our training, our practices, our bodies. We hoard our health, intent on keeping it as long as humanly possible.

But this strikes the tribal elder as a step in the wrong direction. That is, the whole purpose of health is to give it away. Give it away to the tribe and your loved ones. Give it away to the long body. Of course your body will start to decay. Of course you will die. Hoarding one's health is the ultimate foolishness. In a long body world, your only real shot at immortality is through the continued survival of the biosphere and the people living in it. By giving her health to the long body, the warrior fulfills her role. What is health for, if not to spend it on the people and causes that need it?

long rewards

The problem with being a tribal elder is that you aren't going to be rewarded for your efforts, not in a conventional sense, and almost certainly not in your lifetime. The events you set in motion today might take a long time to play out, and successful outcomes won't materialize for years, decades, or even centuries. In a sense, you're working for people who aren't even alive yet. Your seventh-generation descendants may celebrate your efforts, but you won't be around to enjoy the rewards. The seeds you plant today may not germinate for a hundred years.

Obviously, this is something that will take some getting used to. In our conventional, modern lives, we expect to receive our rewards in what might be called "a timely manner." After all, we've been raised in a culture that's saturated with carrots and sticks, a point made famous by educator Alfie Kohn in *Punished by Rewards: The Trouble with Gold Stars, Incentive Plans, A's, Praise and Other Bribes.* As Kohn tells it, most of us have been trained *by* rewards. In other words, we've been trained first and foremost to chase incentives and avoid punishments. In almost every setting, from grade school to the corporate workplace, the basic instruction is always the same: "Do this and you'll get that." If we adopt this as our governing principle for living, life becomes little more than a mindless exercise in stimulus-response.

But things are different when you're working for the seventh generation. You're working hard to sustain the tribe and the future of our blue-green world, but you're almost certainly not going to be rewarded in your lifetime. You're not going to earn a big salary, and even more likely, you're going to be paying out of pocket for transportation, meals, lodging, and everything else that needs to happen. If you're firmly attached to a big payoff, you're going to be unhappy.

Environmental and social activism means sacrificing big chunks of your life for people who haven't even been born, people you will never meet, people who will never be able to thank you. In other words, the warrior's art is highly speculative. In rational, economic terms, it is folly. Who would invest in an outcome they will never see or experience?

But activism is not rational economics. It's something deeper and more powerful. And in this domain, sacrificing for a distant, tribal good isn't folly; it's an act of spiritual intelligence. Giving one's life for downstream improvement not only feeds the greater good, but it also makes us happier and healthier as individuals in this lifetime. The way to be healthier, in other words, is to give your health away.

If you're looking for big, immediate rewards, you're in the wrong line of work. If you're hoping for some kind of tangible payoff in this lifetime, you're going to be disappointed. Instead, you've got to take your sense of satisfaction directly from the activity itself and from the meaning that it holds. In other words, you've got to connect with the intrinsic pleasures that come with activism: working with people, organizing, creating content, and crafting narratives.

It's a tough gig. But that's just the way it is when you're working for the future. Big, audacious goals require a long view. As American theologian Reinhold Neibuhr reminds us, "Nothing that is worth doing can be achieved in our lifetime."

a new golden age

The beauty of getting older is that it gives us perspective. We give up some of our strength, endurance, and vitality, but we also begin to see the world with a far deeper clarity. In fact, growing older is not unlike the process by which our vision adapts to darkness. Think back to the last time you camped out in the mountains. Stepping out into the night air, it usually takes a few minutes to really see the stars. According to experienced star watchers and astronomers, the real clarity of vision doesn't come for an hour or more. But with this adaptation comes a better view, sharper detail, better focus, and above all, a greater appreciation of depth. Subtle features and relationships are revealed.

Turning to another metaphor, growing older is very much like climbing a mountain. With each passing day, the air gets thinner and the steps more difficult, but we're rewarded with a better view of our habitat and our lives. In time, higher altitude gives us vital perspective on our lives and the human predicament. This is how David Brooks put it in *The Road to Character*:

> Intellectual humility is accurate self-awareness from a distance. It is moving over the course of one's life from the adolescent's close-up view of yourself, in which you fill the whole canvas, to a landscape view in which you see, from a wider perspective, your strengths and weaknesses, your connections and dependencies, and the role you play in a larger story.

Being a tribal elder is no easy matter. Conditions are often wicked. Every tribe, organization and community is unique. Tough decisions and judgment calls must be made, usually with incomplete information. Wild animals stalk the tribe, bad weather and wildfires make life difficult. Competing personalities and interests gum up the works. People fight; disputes are common. Uncertainty and ambiguity are constant companions. In this environment, the chances of a misstep are high indeed.

Along the way, you'll sometimes falter and mislead your tribe. You'll misjudge your habitat and the capabilities of your hunters. You'll be strong when you should have been adaptable. You'll be compliant when you should have been steadfast. On occasion, you'll communicate poorly and mix your messages. New information might even reveal that you've been moving in the wrong direction for some time. All of this is quite inevitable.

But no matter how wicked the situation and how deep your confusion, you can lead with a spirit that's earnest, sincere, curious, and compassionate. You can maintain your focus on big health, the long body, and a blue-green future. You will still make mistakes, but in the long view, this is the core of the warrior's art, the thing that endures and inspires. The seventh generation will forgive your screw ups, your missteps, and your awkwardness. But they'll remember the dignity, effort, and sincerity that you brought to the process.

Length Is Strength

A human being is part of a whole, called by us the Universe, a part limited in time and space. He experiences himself, his thoughts and feelings, as something separated from the rest a kind of optical delusion of his consciousness. This delusion is, a kind of prison for us, restricting us to our personal desires and to affection for a few persons nearest us. Our task must be to free ourselves from this prison by widening our circles of compassion to embrace all living creatures and the whole of nature in its beauty.

Albert Einstein

When spiders unite, they can tie up a lion.

Ethiopian proverb

Looking at the state of the world from the vantage point of early 2017, it's easy to despair. So many of the curves are pointed in the wrong direction. The "hockey stick" graph of exponential growth is fast becoming the dominant icon for our time: population, resource consumption and depletion, atmospheric warming, and species extinction are all moving in the wrong direction. American leadership in the world is waning under the chaotic leadership of a reality TV star. We're buried under a mountain of inconvenient facts, and our sense of uncertainty is at an all-time high. Hard times are coming.

promise surrounds us

Nevertheless, there are reasons for long-term optimism. When we zoom out for a larger, historical view, we find that the picture changes, possibly for the better. This is the approach adopted by Steven Pinker in his landmark 2011 book *The Better Angels of Our Nature: Why Violence Has Declined*. Drawing on a mountain of convincing evidence, Pinker identifies several historical forces that have driven declines in violence around the world: the rise of the nation-state with a monopoly on the legitimate use of force, the development of commerce and the understanding that peace is better for business, the women's rights movement, cosmopolitanism and the spread of literacy and learning, and the increasing application of knowledge and reason in human affairs. Together, these forces have increased our ability to coexist.

Pinker's conclusions are surprising, but his argument is persuasive and optimistic. Maybe we can take a similar approach and look for historical and cultural forces that will contribute to ecological and social transformation of the long body. When historians of the future write the history of the twenty-first century, perhaps they'll point to these forces of transformation:

a new biological awareness

Appearances to the contrary, a new ecological awareness is in fact sweeping across the planet, especially in the minds of young people. Beginning with the spectacular Earth-from-space imagery of 1969, more and more people are thinking in planetary and ecological terms. More recently, concern over climate change has led to unprecedented acts of cross-border global cooperation, especially in treaties such as the Paris Accords. Mass marches for climate sanity, women's rights, and science are becoming increasingly commonplace.

We are also seeing a distinct philosophical shift in human identity and the old duality of "humans vs. animals." Once a bedrock of modern culture, human exceptionalism has steadily been eroding over the last several decades as more and more evidence comes to light showing the true depth of our animal nature. People are becoming increasingly comfortable with big biological time scales and the epic events in Earth history. We're becoming fluent with ideas like fossil digs, extinction events, asteroid strikes, common ancestors, and radiocarbon dating.

Discoveries by Jane Goodall and books by primatologist Frans de Waal have been particularly influential in breaking down the human–animal divide. In most quarters, the statement "humans are animals" is no longer considered heretical or even particularly controversial. It is now acceptable to talk about one's animal nature or Neanderthal heritage in polite company.

It is commonplace to refer to chimpanzees and bonobos as our closest living relatives. In time, this view will surely become more widespread, and in turn, more of us will look for biological solutions for biological problems.

Also encouraging is the proliferation of primal fitness and natural movement training programs. Around the world, more and more trainers are taking their clients out of the gym and into the outdoors where they belong. Programs such as MovNat, Wildfitness, and Evolve, Move, Play show that natural outdoor training is both fun and functional.Likewise, groups like the Ancestral Health Society are bringing physicians into the fold, showing the virtues of Paleo-style living in a modern context.

one health

Another welcome development is the emerging One Health perspective. This medical paradigm recognizes that the health of domestic animals, wildlife, and people are inextricably linked to one another and the environment. One Health is a unifying concept that brings together human health care practitioners, veterinarians, and public and environmental health professionals.

The history of One Health goes back at least as far as the late nineteenth century, when German physician and pathologist Rudolf Virchow wrote: "Between animal and human medicine there is no dividing line, nor should there be. The object is different, but the experience obtained constitutes the basis of all medicine."

In 1947, veterinarian James Steele established the field of veterinary public health at the Centers for Disease Control. The phrase "One Medicine" first appeared in the textbook *Veterinary Medicine and Human Health*. In 2003, Dr. William Karesh, founder of the EcoHealth Alliance, coined the term "One Health," and in 2007, the American Veterinary Medical Association and the American Medical Association began collaborating. Today, organizations supporting the One Health perspective include the American Medical Association, American Veterinary Medical Association, the Centers for Disease Control and Prevention, the United States Department of Agriculture, the National Oceanic and Atmospheric Administration, and the US's National Environmental Health Association. More than 850 prominent scientists, physicians, and veterinarians worldwide have endorsed the initiative.

The beauty of One Health is the way it integrates our interest in the long body. In effect, it radically expands the "scope of practice" for health and medical professionals. This "big medicine" approach is new to our Western ears, but it represents a profoundly important step in the right direction.

connecting habitat with corridors

We can also take inspiration from the development of wildlife corridors that are now appearing around the world. Sometimes called habitat corridors or green corridors, these structures connect wildlife habitat separated by human activity. The great thing about corridors is that they allow an exchange of individuals between populations. This helps prevent the negative effects of inbreeding and reduced genetic diversity. Many conservationists now advocate for corridors as our best bet for saving species and wild lands.

Wildlife corridors are essential in maintaining biodiversity and in turn, stability and strength of populations. Animals can move from one area to another to find food, refuge, and mating opportunities. Isolated areas of habitat, once they're connected by a bridge or underpass, become larger and healthier. The whole becomes greater than the sum of its separate, individual parts.

These kinds of corridors are now in use around the world. In 2001, a wolf corridor was opened through a golf course in Jasper National Park in Alberta, Canada. In Washington State, a major wildlife overpass is under construction over Interstate 90. In Southern California, underpasses and drainage culverts have been effective. Numerous corridors have been opened in Europe. There is now a China–Russia Tiger Corridor. At last count, there are eighty-eight elephant corridors in India.

The actual effectiveness of wildlife corridors, overpasses, and underpasses is difficult to measure and a matter of some dispute. But there can be no denying their psycho-spiritual and symbolic benefits. The mere presence of a corridor has a powerfully beneficial effect, not just on habitat and animals, but on the human mind and culture. The implicit message is clear: We value nature enough to give it passage. We're creating room for the rest of creation. It's an act of respect and humility. These corridors would be worth the effort for no other reason. And it's a far better move than building arbitrary walls along national borders.

the greening of business and religion

Another development that gives us hope is the increasing emphasis on sustainable, planet-friendly business practices around the world. While most companies seem stuck in conventional, profit-centric business models, it now appears that many are actually pursuing a triple bottom line of "people, planet, profit." A notable leader in this effort is B the Change Media, which offers companies certification as public benefit corporations and the coveted "Circle B" designation. Applicants must follow a rigorous set of standards and accounting on issues of sustainability, clean energy, and workers' rights. There are currently 1,008 companies that have met these standards of transparency, as well as of social and environmental performance.

Of course, we are right to be skeptical, and corporate greenwashing is often nothing more than a feel-good marketing layer designed to lure customers. We might even wonder how capitalism in any form could be a solution to our predicament. After all, the free market is a driver of some of the most egregious crimes against the planet. This is precisely the point made by Naomi Klein in *This Changes Everything: Capitalism vs. the Climate*. Klein argues that the market has not—and cannot—fix the climate crisis, but will instead make things worse with ever more extreme and ecologically damaging extraction methods. Klein has called for a complete revision of what she terms "disaster capitalism."

So maybe the "greening" of business is simply lipstick on a bullet train to catastrophe, but it's also the case that a good many companies and entrepreneurs are doing valuable pro-social and pro-habitat work. And while capitalism may in fact be a deeply flawed model, we've got to work with what we've got on hand. Radical changes are called for, but in the meantime, incremental changes are good too.

We can also take heart in the increasing embrace of environmental activism by traditional religions. Voices from a variety of spiritual traditions are forging a fresh link between religion and environmental and social activism. Some activists are even suggesting that "God is green."

This may well come as a surprise. Religion and environmentalism have long been considered strange bedfellows. The world's Abrahamic traditions—Christianity, Judaism and Islam—have rarely acted as advocates for the natural world. In fact, some critics charge that Western traditions actually paved the way for exploitation of our planet by providing Biblical justification for human domination. Likewise, some evangelicals dismiss our earthly concerns as irrelevant, focusing instead on the afterlife.

But there is, in fact, a green history in the Christian tradition. Saint Francis of Assisi (1181–1226) was an Italian Roman Catholic friar and preacher who famously believed that nature itself was the mirror of God. He called all creatures his "brothers" and "sisters" and even preached to the birds. In his "Canticle of the Creatures" ("Praises of Creatures"), he sounds positively indigenous when he mentions "Brother Sun" and "Sister Moon." In 1979, Pope John Paul II declared St. Francis the Patron Saint of Ecology.

More recently, Pope Francis has called for urgent action to stop climate change, and proposed that caring for the environment be added to the traditional Christian works of mercy, such as feeding the hungry and visiting the sick. In his 2015 Encyclical, "On Care for Our Common Home," Francis called for an "ecological conversion" for the faithful. Not surprisingly, Francis has taken St. Francis of Assisi as a guide and inspiration.

In his 2015 address to the UN, Francis affirmed the rights for the environment. "It must be stated that a true 'right of the environment' does exist ... Any harm done to the environment, therefore is harm done to humanity." In August of that year, the Vatican announced a World Day of Prayer for the Care of Creation. "As Christians we wish to offer our contribution towards overcoming the ecological crisis which humanity is living through," Francis wrote. Describing the "ecological crisis" currently underway, the Pope said the event would provide "a precious opportunity to renew our personal participation in this vocation as custodians of creation."

Francis has characterized concerns about the environment as "one of the greatest challenges of our time"—a challenge that is theological, as well as political, in nature. "When I look at ... so many forests, all cut, that have become land ... that can no longer give life," he reflected, "This is our sin, exploiting the Earth... This is one of the greatest challenges of our time: to convert ourselves to a type of development that knows how to respect creation."

Even evangelicals are getting on board. In July 2015, more than 170 evangelical leaders sent President Barack Obama a letter backing a Clean Power Plan to reduce carbon dioxide emissions from coal-burning power plants. Evangelical Christians have emphasized Biblical mandates concerning humanity's role as steward for the caretaking of Creation. The movement is best known for its focus on addressing climate action from a Biblically grounded theological perspective. The Evangelical Climate Initiative argues that human-induced climate change will have severe consequences, and that God's mandate to Adam to care for the Garden of Eden also applies to evangelicals today.

Many in the green religion movement cite the work of Thomas Berry as inspiration. Berry (1914–2009) was a Catholic priest, cultural historian, and ecotheologian. An advocate of "ecospirituality," he is famous for proposing the idea that a deep understanding of the history of the evolving universe is a necessary inspiration and guide for our own functioning as individuals and as a species. Berry believed that humanity, after generations spent in self-glorification and despoiling the world, is poised to embrace a new role as a vital part of a larger, interdependent "communion of subjects" on earth and in the universe. As he put it, "Our challenge is to create a new language, even a new sense of what it is to be human. It is to transcend not only national limitations, but even our species isolation, to enter into the larger community of living species. This brings about a completely new sense of reality and value."

Some of the most notable work in the world of "green religion" is by Michael Dowd, author of *Thank God for Evolution*. Dowd describes himself as a "pro-future evangelist" and a proponent of ecological Christianity. Dowd teaches that "God is synonymous with reality" and that God's work is revealed through scientific evidence. Evidence, in other words, is modern-day scripture.

For Dowd, the prime objective of humanity should be to *live in accord with reality.* Scientific, historic, and cross-cultural discoveries, discerned through global collective intelligence, are *evidential revelation.* Dowd urges us to "stop thinking of theology apart from ecology." "Limits are sacred and must be honored... The environment is not our surrounding, it's our source." Naturally, Dowd has detractors on both the "science side" and the "religion side," but this does not diminish the power of his perspective. His attempts at integration are useful, and for many, inspiring.

It remains to be seen whether this new alliance will amount to real change, and obviously, the greening of religion is not an ultimate solution for everyone. Traditionalists will no doubt stick to their conventions, and atheists will continue to reject the notion that religion has anything to offer. But for many, this is a promising and inspiring step. Anything that brings people into greater harmony with the land must be considered a good thing, regardless of your spiritual inclinations.

If religion is going green, so too is Hollywood. While it's true that the movie industry continues to churn out more than its share of "apocalypse porn" and mindless disaster flicks, there are some powerful exceptions. The 2009 film *Avatar* laid bare our cultural bias towards domination of the natural world, as it offered a powerful depiction of indigenous-primal culture. In the Navi people, producer James Cameron created a new-old narrative of physical athleticism, coupled with intense intimacy with the natural world. The message resonated with audiences around the world. Likewise, Conservation International's production of "Nature is Speaking" is incredibly powerful. Various celebrities give voice to habitats: Julia Roberts is "Mother Nature," Harrison Ford is "Ocean," Kevin Spacey is "The Rainforest." The message is simple and profound: "Nature doesn't need us; we need nature."

the neuroplastic revolution

Another promising development comes from the world of neuroscience and neurobiology. Now, for the first time in history, we have a solid understanding of how the nervous system works, how people learn and how to train ourselves for better adaptation. We are entering a new golden age of training and practice, an era that promises to rewrite everything we thought we knew about human performance and potential.

We now understand that neuro-fatalism, the pessimistic dogma of a static, unchanging nervous system, is dead. Starting in the late 20th century, a series of groundbreaking discoveries demonstrated conclusively that the human brain is a highly dynamic, "plastic" organ that changes itself constantly throughout life. Synapses continuously remodel themselves into new patterns of activity, insulating myelin sheaths grow thicker with use, and new neurons are generated from stem cells.

This new view, now known as neuro-optimism, has taken the scientific and popular imagination by storm, and the message is deeply empowering. We now know that we can take control of our learning and development. We can learn new arts, skills and disciplines throughout life. We can transform our brains, our bodies, and our spirits. With training, we can develop almost any quality we desire. All it takes are quality reps.

We are witnessing nothing less than the emergence of a new educational paradigm. When we couple the discoveries of modern neuroscience with the transformative practices of Eastern tradition, we come to the conclusion that almost any quality of mind, body, or spirit can be sculpted by practice. We may not be able to change our hair or eye color, but when it comes to the really important qualities of our bodies and life experience, it's all there waiting for us, open to refinement through training and practice.

In this sense, we might even say that, when it comes to the important qualities that define our mind, bodies, spirits, and lives, "it's all muscle." We know we can make our muscles bigger and stronger with a regular program of sets and reps, but that's just the beginning; almost every system in the body behaves similarly. Bones get dense with vigorous use, nerve cell circuits get faster, and metabolism becomes more efficient. And, since the mind, body, and spirit are intimately interconnected, it's safe to say that the entire system is trainable. Whether it's our ability to lift a heavy weight or produce a state of compassion, kindness, happiness, resilience, courage, love, willpower, or focused attention, it's all trainable. The opportunity for growth and transformation is vast.

Whatever the future holds, we can rely upon the fundamentals of learning and adaptation. Conditions may well become arduous and extremely inconvenient. Will we have to walk long distances once again? Get by with less? Manage our lives with simpler tools? Do more physical labor? Improvise new technologies? Eat new foods? We might well resist these changes at first, but our bodies will learn. We can and will adapt.

native resurgence and red-white alliance

There's more good news. A new generation of indigenous activists is making effective use of social media to organize and speak out. Tireless work by people such as Winona LaDuke, executive director of Honor the Earth, and Standing Rock Sioux chairman David Archambault II, is making a difference. So too is Tom Goldtooth, executive director of the Indigenous Environmental Network, one of the most influential Native non-governmental organizations in the country. Native voices are having an impact.

We're also beginning to see promising new alliances between native people, environmentalists and social justice advocates around the world. Climate leaders such as Bill McKibben are supporting native rights and activists are unifying around core issues of environmental preservation and social justice.

The events at Standing Rock Indian Reservation in North Dakota were symbolic of this new alliance. In the spring of 2016, a grassroots movement began protesting the construction of the Dakota Access Pipeline. (Aka the "black snake") Over the summer, the camp grew to thousands of people, a diversity of native tribes and non-native supporters. Throughout the fall, solidarity rallies and marches were held in cities across the country. In November, hundreds of cities held protests against the pipeline in a coordinated action. Hundreds of protesters gathered peacefully in Chicago, Seattle, Los Angeles, Manhattan, Denver, and other cities; dozens were arrested.

Support for the movement even crossed conventional political lines. In September of 2016, Senator Bernie Sanders spoke to a crowd of about three thousand members of the Standing Rock Sioux Tribe and supporters at a protest outside the White House. Photographs of local protests around the country show substantial non-native support. Groups supporting Standing Rock include Physicians for Social Responsibility, 350.org, the International League of Conservation Photographers, and virtually every climate and environmental action group. Thousands of people of all colors now refer to themselves as "water protectors."

In January 2017, Donald Trump signed an executive order authorizing completion of the pipeline, and the Standing Rock camp was later cleared. The defeat was a crushing setback, but all is not lost. Standing Rock endures as a symbolic rallying point, and supporters are reorganizing new actions at sites around the country and the world. The summer of 2017 will surely be a season of renewed effort and red-white activism. Going forward, people of all colors may well take heart from the words of Crazy Horse:

> Upon suffering beyond suffering, the Red Nation shall
> rise again and it shall be a blessing for a sick world.
> A world filled with broken promises, selfishness and
> separations. A world longing for light again. I see a time
> of seven generations when all the colors of mankind will

gather under the sacred Tree of Life and the whole Earth will become one circle again. In that day there will be those among the Lakota who will carry knowledge and understanding of unity among all living things, and the young white ones will come to those of my people and ask for this wisdom. I salute the light within your eyes where the whole universe dwells. For when you are at that center within you and I am in that place within me, we shall be as one.

never one thing

The least movement is of importance to all nature. The entire ocean is affected by a pebble.

Blaise Pascal (1623–1662)

As we reflect on the state of our planet and our role in a long body world, we begin to ask new questions about our power and potential. We become increasingly suspicious of conventional stories of isolated individuals, dwarfed by immense forces and institutions that are utterly beyond our control. No longer do we see our behaviors as limited in space and time. When life is radically interdependent, anything becomes possible. Our powers may well be longer and more substantial than we think.

Inspiration for this perspective comes from the work of ecologist Garrett Hardin (1915–2003). Hardin was famous for his 1968 description of "the tragedy of the commons," but he also coined one of the most powerful phrases ever to come out of the ecology movement. Struck by the interdependence he observed at every level of ecosystem dynamics, he concluded, "We can never do merely one thing."

This phrase not only accurately describes our large-scale impacts on forests, grasslands, and oceans; it also inspires a new appreciation of our potential as activists. It reminds us of a primal truth: Everything we do in this world and our personal lives has consequences. Every thing we touch, say, or think impacts the world, sometimes in surprisingly powerful ways.

Given what we now know about ecology, interpersonal neurobiology, and other sciences, it's safe to generalize: Everything ripples. Every action creates grooves and ruts, both inside our bodies and outside in the natural and human world. We cut paths in the world with our choices and our thoughts. Every action, no matter how subtle, has consequences. Even inaction cascades through our lives. No action is truly neutral; even acts of passivity have effects on bodies, people, communities, and environments.

This cascading effect is about far more than what we do to large-scale ecosystems. Of course, it's easy to understand that building a dam is "not one thing." A massive concrete structure that chokes a major river is certain to have a multitude of destructive ecosystem consequences that ripple across habitats and species, in space and time. But the same principle applies to the seemingly minor acts of our everyday lives, things we rarely think of as "ecological." A word, a gesture, a kindness, or an extra effort; all of these things ripple and cascade through our lives and the lives of the people around us. No matter how insignificant they might seem at the moment, they are never "just one thing."

The effects are more powerful than we imagine. Many of us understand the fact that our overt behaviors will have consequences; steal from your neighbor and you'll poison the trust in your community, clear-cut a forest and you destroy the watershed. But it's not just physical actions that cascade through the flux and flow of our lives. Even the slightest whispers of thought can do it too. We now know that the actions of the mind actually shape neural connections, a constant sculpting, honing, growing, and re-forming of neural circuits that goes on in every moment of our lives. In other words, our very thoughts have tissue-level consequences. And when brain tissue changes, so do cognition, memory, learning, and behavior. And when behavior changes, so do social systems. No thought is without consequence.

This is where ecology and the art of personal living intersect with chaos theory. While very few of us truly understand the science of complexity, fractals, strange attractors, and the like, most of us can grasp the "butterfly effect." As scientists tell it, the atmosphere of the Earth is so radically interconnected and sensitive to initial conditions that "the flap of a butterfly's wings in Texas can set off a thunderstorm on the other side of the world." This is a fabulous image, of course, but it also happens to be an accurate description of how complex systems change. When systems become hyper-complex (atmospheres, habitats, human brains, and communities), minute disturbances can trigger immense, large-scale transformations. In complex systems, little things can be enormous.

In our weaker moments, many of us complain about our powerlessness, especially in the worlds of politics and power. We don't have the looks or the talent or the money to make a difference. But in fact, every human is a creative agent. We are sculpting our bodies, our brains, and the world continuously throughout our lives. Every moment has potential. Every act of courage, no matter how small, has consequences. All of us are involved in creating the world, all the time. The only thing left is to ask: What kind of world are we creating in this moment?

Of course it's easy to despair in the face of overwhelming odds. When we compare our personal ability to effect change with cultural inertia and the power of the status quo, our efforts sometimes feel like a candle against the sun. At times, even our best efforts feel irrelevant and meaningless.

Perhaps another metaphor will help. In 1962, philosopher Thomas Kuhn wrote *The Structure of Scientific Revolutions*. At the time, most people thought of scientific progress simply as the accumulation of knowledge, a process in which new evidence builds on established structure, brick by brick, fact by fact. In contrast, Kuhn argued for an episodic model in which periods of continuity are interrupted by periods of revolutionary discovery and re-imagining.

This revolutionary process begins with the appearance of minor, inconvenient "anomalies" that seem to contradict established knowledge. At the outset, this countervailing evidence goes largely ignored and even ridiculed, but over time, the weight accumulates, leading eventually to a sudden and dramatic shift in thinking and attention. For Kuhn, this is precisely what played out in the Copernican revolution, beginning in 1543. When Copernicus first proposed a heliocentric solar system, the evidence was actually rather weak, and few people embraced the new perspective. It was only later, when Galileo filled in gaps in the model, that it took on the power to overthrow the existing paradigm.

In essence, Kuhn argued that the process of scientific and cultural change operates like an enormous balance scale. A scientist or activist adds a contradictory idea to one side of the scale, but nothing seems to happen. People add more evidence and more activism, and still nothing happens. The process may continue for some time, and during this period, the scientist–activist may well conclude that his efforts are having no effect. He may even conclude that his work has no meaning.

But the grains of sand add up, and shifts do come, sometimes in an instant. In 1991, the former Soviet Union collapsed almost overnight under the weight of its own incompetence. In 2015, same-sex marriage reached a sudden tipping point of popular acceptance. Similarly, mass acceptance of the reality of climate change appears to be taking hold. For years, scientific evidence poured in with no apparent change in public opinion, but today, only the most committed delusionaries reject the reality of climate change.

This is how natural systems work as well. Small changes accumulate without perceptible change, but eventually a tipping point is reached. Vegetation and animal life change slowly, then radically. Our personal lives grow in similar ways. Individual growth is not a linear progression of insights that build upon each other. Challenging information falls into our lives and often goes ignored. It happens again, then again. But sooner or later, the dissonance builds to a point where it can no longer be ignored. One day, we experience a personal paradigm shift, sometimes even a Copernican transformation in the meaning of our lives and our relationships with the world.

All of this should give us a sense of hope. The grain of sand you drop upon the scale may look and feel invisible. But it is not nothing. You may not see the effect, even in your lifetime. But the scale will move as people add their grains of effort and courage. Don't despair. Sooner or later, the paradigm will shift, and the shift may be bigger, faster, and more significant than you think.

In the end, it's all about the doing. Times are hard and the odds are long. Conditions are overwhelming. Our biosphere is in mortal danger. But the odds have always been long for the warrior. The quest is always uncertain, the outcome unknown. Risk is inevitable, and the chance of failure is substantial. Still, the warrior must fight.

In the long run, resignation is worse than defeat. Apathy is a kind of death unto itself. Once we give up, the meaning drains from our lives like the blood that flows from a wounded body. But there is meaning and health in fighting. Fighting keeps us strong. Defeat in battle is acceptable, but resignation is not.

Dylan Thomas had it right. Do not go gentle. Rage, rage against the dying of our blue-green home. Rage, rage against social injustice. Do not go gentle into depression, trivial amusement, or distraction. Do not go gentle into apathy, cynicism, or resignation. No matter how difficult this battle becomes, you must not give up. This is a fight worth fighting.

General Principles

Sometimes it's easy to get lost in the immensity of the long body and the chaos of modern life. Mismatch often leaves us confused about where to turn, how to behave and even who we are. If you find yourself lost in this new wilderness, go back to these general principles for long body health:

It's the relationship, human!

This is the place to begin. Question your relationship with your body, your habitat, your tribe and your culture. Relationships are the raw material of your art.

Take the long view

Embrace the totality of body, habitat, tribe, and culture. It's all one body. The whole world is kin.

Make your life relevant

Can you draw a line between your profession and making a difference in the state of the world? Don't put up with an irrelevant career. It's bad for the planet, and it's bad for your life.

Put your body where your mouth is

Adopt an attitude of radical responsibility. The warrior activist is responsible for *everything*. The more responsibility you accept, the more meaningful your life becomes.

Harness the power of mismatch

The mismatch between our ancient bodies and the modern world is an acute stressor. But there's power in this predicament. Use the contrast to fire your curiosity and your search for meaning. The flip side of stress is energy.

Do unto the world…

…as you would have the world do unto you. In a long body world, every action reflects. All behaviors are boomerangs. Treat people and the Earth the way you would like to be treated. Do unto yourself as you would have the world do unto you.

Go outside

Get out of the house, the car, and the office at every opportunity. Don't wait for the good weather. Get the right clothes and expose yourself to nature. Outdoors is where the health is.

Stay close to your body

Don't drift too far from your primal nature. Refresh the connection to your physicality often. Practice movement snacks whenever you can. Do the activist workout.

Eat real food

Avoid the edible food-like products. Seek out "earth food" that connects you to habitat and people.

Seek contrast

Avoid chronic, flat-line efforts. Push into challenge with all you've got, then relax deeply into comfort and rejuvenation. Rest more, sleep more. Do less.

True the wheel

Honor interdependence. Balance the whole structure of every system you're a part of. Strengthen what's weak. Lengthen what's short.

Question and create culture

Don't passively accept the culture that's handed to you. Remember, our culture was built by people no smarter than yourself. If Mother Culture is wrong, call her on it. You too can have a hand in the future.

The enemy is never wrong

The people around us are never wrong. The situation is never wrong. These things simply are. Get over your outrage, adjust your strategies, and get back to work. Keep adapting.

Tell a better story

Edit your narratives about the human experience and your life. Tell a story of integration, meaning, and activism. Practice narrative medicine with new perspectives on injury and illness. The cure for bad stories is better stories.

Become a tribal elder

As you age, take a leadership role in your tribe's survival. Your life becomes more and more valuable with each passing year. Step up to greater responsibility.

Exercise kindness and compassion

We're all in this mismatched predicament together. Everyone's body is ancient; everyone is struggling to adapt. All of us are misfits to some degree. No one really knows how to manage this strange and unprecedented world. Have patience with yourself and those around you.

Be a good ancestor

Life your life as your descendants would wish. Work for the seventh generation.

Afterwords

Books are an illusion. One person's name goes on the cover, but the writing and ideas are inevitably long. Influence flows from habitat and community into the body and fingers of the writer, waxing and waning with the movement of culture and the arc of history. Ideas coalesce in the mind and words of an individual, but it's always a group effort. We all played a part in this one. In particular, I'd like to thank my favorite warrior activists for their assistance and inspirations:

Ray Sylvester, Pete Karabetis, Chandler Stevens, Steve and Carla Laskevitch, Travis Janeway, Mike Zwack, Dana Lyons, Kwame Brown, Aaron Blaisdell, Mitch Friedman, Dan Spencer, Cain Credicott, Rafe Kelly, Bill McKibben, Tim DeChristopher, Michael Dowd, Jim Collins, Paul Ranson, Ed Drax, Tara Wood, Steve Myrland, Robert Sapolsky, Mike and Tanya Levy, Vincent Thibault, Sam, Beth, Alex, and Travis Forencich, Susan Fahringer and Keith Worman, Dawni Rae and Alia Joy Shaw.And most of all, Mom. I so wish you could see this.

Bibliography

Big History: The Big Bang, Life on Earth, and the Rise of Humanity by David Christian (audio CD by The Great Courses)

Biology and Human Behavior: The Neurological Origins of Individuality, 2nd Edition by Robert Sapolsky

Crazy Like Us: The Globalization of the American Psyche by Ethan Watters

Deep Survival: Who Lives, Who Dies, and Why by Laurence Gonzales

Ecopsychology: Restoring the Earth, Healing the Mind edited by Theodore Roszak

Go Wild: Free Your Body and Mind From the Afflictions of Civilization by John Ratey MD and Richard Manning

Medical Nemesis by Ivan Illich

Mindset: The New Psychology of Success by Carol Dweck

Narrative Medicine: The Use of History and Story in the Healing Process by Lewis Mehl-Madrona

Presence: Bringing Your Boldest Self to Your Biggest Challenges by Amy Cuddy

Punished by Rewards: The Trouble with Gold Stars, Incentive Plans, A's, Praise and Other Bribes by Alfie Kohn

Red Alert!: Saving the Planet with Indigenous Knowledge by Daniel R. Wildcat

Sapiens: A Brief History of Humankind by Yuval Noah Harari

The Songlines by Bruce Chatwin

Spark: The Revolutionary New Science of Exercise and the Brain by John Ratey

Surviving Survival: The Art and Science of Resilience by Laurence Gonzales

The As if Principle: The Radically New Approach to Changing Your Life by Richard Wiseman

The Invisible Gorilla: And Other Ways Our Intuitions Deceive Us by Christopher Chabris and Daniel Simons

The Better Angels of Our Nature by Steven Pinker

The Myth Gap: What Happens When Evidence and Arguments Aren't Enough? by Alex Evans

The Neurobiology of "We" by Daniel J. Siegel, M.D.

The Old Way: A Story of the First People by Elizabeth Marshall Thomas

The Spirit Catches You and You Fall Down: A Hmong Child, Her American Doctors, and the Collision of Two Cultures by Anne Radioman

The Story of the Human Body: Evolution, Health and Disease by Daniel Liberman

The Upside of Stress: Why Stress Is Good For You And How To Get Good At It by Kelly McGonigal

Tribe: On Homecoming and Belonging by Sebastian Junger

When the Body Says No: The Cost of Hidden Stress by Gabor Maté, M.D.

Why Zebras Don't Get Ulcers: The Acclaimed Guide to Stress, Stress-Related Diseases and Coping Third Edition by Robert Sapolsky

Willful Blindness: Why We Ignore the Obvious at Our Peril by Margaret Heffernan

Zoobiquity: What Animals Can Teach Us About Health and the Science of Healing by Barbara Patterson-Horowitz

Notes

For notes and references, including clickable links, see the Exuberant Animal website: www.exuberantanimal.com

About Exuberant Animal

Exuberant Animal® offers training in big health and warrior activism. If you're a trainer, coach, movement teacher, or health professional, contact us for information about training and workshops. Frank Forencich is also available for presentations and custom trainings. Visit exuberantanimal.com for details.

Notable Activist Organizations

International Dark Sky Association

Union of Concerned Scientists

350.org

Physicians for Social Responsibility

The Action Network

The Center for Artistic Activism

International League of Conservation Photographers

Environmental Defense Fund

Ancestral Health Society

One Health

Earth Charter

Conservation International

Indigenous Environmental Network

Sierra Club

The Center for Earth Jurisprudence

Honor Earth

Doctors Without Borders

Center for Biological Diversity

Earth First!

Conservation Northwest

Beautiful Trouble

Sea Shepherd Conservation Society

Leonardo DiCaprio Foundation

Adbusters Media Foundation